GENERAL DRAFTING

Nuclear Electric Generating Plant at San Onofre, California (Courtesy, Southern California Edison Company)
The planning of this plant involved hundreds of drawings made by mechanical, electrical, sheet-metal, and architectural draftsmen.
Draftsmanship is the transition from conception to production . . .

VERNE C. FRYKLUND, Ph. D.
Emeritus President, Stout University
Menomonie, Wisconsin

FRANK ROY KEPLER, B. S.
Supervisor of Drafting, Retired
Detroit, Michigan

GENERAL DRAFTING

McKNIGHT & McKNIGHT
Publishing Company
Bloomington, Illinois

FOURTH EDITION
COPYRIGHT 1969

Third Edition, 1960
Eight Printings

COPYRIGHT 1938, 1949, 1960, 1969

by McKnight & McKnight Publishing Company

Lithographed in U.S.A.

Library of Congress
Card Catalog Number 78-81375

Foreword

As advances are made in technology, new techniques for making drawings, educating workmen, and setting up machines are necessary. Innovations in the making and reading of drawings are being made for computers and for courses in drafting. Photography and microfilm are used in computers to record and provide information obtained from drawings. Procedures of presenting information can be provided in experiences with improved methods presented in courses in drafting. Courses in drafting provide experiences that contribute to the understanding of procedures in formulating quicker methods of presenting information for construction in industry. Without working drawings the ideas for these improved methods could not have been presented.

The lessons in this book were prepared for teaching the fundamental practices of general drafting. *General Drafting* includes the various applications of sketching and mechanical drawing as related to many kinds of activities that require working drawings.

This book fills a need that has frequently been expressed to the authors in varied contacts with drafting teachers; it is a text that covers the fundamentals of drafting, based upon an analysis of the activity. It is unusual to find a book that actually gives instruction on *how to perform* the fundamentals. To have visual and written instructions and problems covering both the principles and the fundamentals of drafting makes this book doubly useful and flexible in its service.

It should be noted that immediate application in the use of drafting instruments and geometrical forms is evident in this book. Therefore, drafting instruments and construction of geometrical forms are not presented in separate units but as they are applied. The use of each tool in its own drafting situation makes learning more certain and more interesting.

General Drafting can be used in connection with any teaching methods, whether on an individual or on a group basis. The problems are suggestive, and the drafting teacher can easily provide more problems when needed. However, there are enough problems in this book to provide a wide range of choice.

General Drafting has been written with a view to make every drawing a problem to be solved. Naturally, it is most desirable practically to work from the actual objects, and whenever an individual pupil needs such assistance the teacher should secure objects and use them, especially at the start.

The problems in *General Drafting* have been presented so as to serve in the same way as would the actual objects. The problems have been numbered in order of complexity, and in a simple way, so that any system of problem assignment or numbering that a teacher may use in assigning problems to better cope with individual differences may be adopted. However, the order of presentation of the various areas of drafting is not by sequence. Some teachers, after covering the instruction in elementary mechanical drafting, may choose to cover map drafting or house planning or sheet metal drafting or another area.

To further enhance the problem-solving characteristics of *General Drafting*, the instructional units are grouped according to the requirements of the problems to be drawn. The student makes immediate application of the instruction to solve a problem. This planned sequence of instruction in the fundamentals of drawing stimulates student interest in the subject as it quickly gives him the practice needed for learning.

This book has been prepared much in the manner of a course of study for beginners. There have been guiding aims conceived from well-known educational and industrial educational aims. The subject aims were guides in the preparation of these instructions and in the choice of problems. These aims are:

1. To provide experiences in the use of drafting instruments and materials in the performance of drafting fundamentals applied to making working drawings.
2. To give occupational information about a variety of drafting occupations and activities dependent upon drafting.
3. To give training in the use of working drawings; and, particularly to foster the habit of making sketches and drawings for conveying ideas to others.
4. To develop an appreciation for the relationships made possible by drawings, of industrial planning, processes, and organization.
5. To provide opportunities for developing usable techniques when individual diagnosis indicates need for such procedure.
6. To develop habits of independent and methodical procedure in the making of drawings.
7. To foster interest in and appreciation of the importance of mathematics as applied to drafting.

In any particular activity where creative work is necessary, the things created become existent because someone knows the fundamentals required in order to accomplish the desired end. Someone is able to apply the fundamentals of the activity in the problems at hand. Drafting is such a creative field of activity, and the fundamentals of drafting should be learned so well that they can be applied in the making of sketches and drawings.

The fundamentals of a particular activity consist of operations and information topics. The operations are manipulative in nature and the information topics are things that must be known. In drafting, a combination of these fundamentals is necessary in the making of working drawings. A certain fund of information of a broadening nature concerning drafting in general, but which is not necessary for successful performance of the work, is also desirable.

Instruction in dimensioning working drawings should include decimals as well as fractions be-cause both are needed. When drawing is done for precise manufacture, decimals are used in most industries, but in architecture fractional dimensioning is common. Both methods should be taught, and the reason for teaching them should be explained to students. It should be understood that not all students who take a first course in drafting are likely to become engineers or draftsmen. Some may enter other occupations with a general and varied experience in several areas of drafting. Therefore, both methods of dimensioning are included in this book.

Method is relative, but success in instruction depends in large measure upon an important principle. In drafting, as in other industrial activities, the teacher must distinguish clearly his responsibilities and the learner's responsibilities in connection with instruction. The teacher *must teach* the fundamentals and the learner *must solve* the problems. In drafting, these problems consist of making working drawings. The latter means that the learner must plan his procedure, which in drafting is represented in large measure by the preliminary sketch made of every working drawing. This is basic to all good teaching of drafting. Many teaching techniques can be and should be employed to make effective the instructions covering the fundamentals and their applications. Individual differences in learning demand ingenuity on the part of the teacher in matching desires and techniques to individual peculiarities in learning.

The vocabulary has been selected to avoid the use of words beyond the attainable understanding of the student. There are a few words, especially of a technical nature, that may tax the average pupil. However, that is to be expected, and even planned for, in arranging progressive learning situations.

Test questions of a study nature have been added at the end of each unit. The test questions provided in this book can be reconstructed and used in various ways, as well as repeated, in making the formal achievement tests. The questions are supplied in limited number and kind with the view to permitting the teacher to conceive new ones.

THE AUTHORS

Acknowledgements

The success of good books is always more certain because of assistance given the authors by persons and organizations that provide a measure of quality that authors cannot readily give alone. In preparation of the first edition of this book, the authors are glad to make the following acknowledgements:

Mr. Francis L. Zwickey, a teacher of drafting in Denby High school, Detroit, Michigan, made the working drawings and the pictorial drawings of the problems. Mr. Jack Kentta, teacher of drawing in Austin High School, Austin, Minnesota, made most of the sketches covering the fundamentals. Mr. Shirley L. Owens, formerly Head of the Department of Vocational Education at the Jefferson Intermediate School, Detroit, Michigan, a registered architect and member of the Dearborn Planning Commission, gave valuable suggestions regarding the architectural section.

In the second edition, Mr. E. Ross Awry made the drawings of the small home in the architectural section. Mr. Harold A. Stormzand of the Electrical Department, Cass Technical High School, Detroit, Michigan, and Dr. Phillip Ruehl of Stout State University, Menomonie, Wisconsin, furnished the sketches for the wiring diagrams and the electrical symbols. Mr. Richard M. Carlsen, formerly a teacher of drafting at Hutchins Intermediate School, and now Principal of the Wilson Junior High School, Detroit, Michigan, permitted use of certain problems. Mr. Earl Phillips of Mumford High School, Detroit, Michigan, made valuable suggestions for the third edition. There were many organizations whose contributions are indicated in appropriate places throughout the book.

Contents

Curves, Circles, and Circular Forms

Electrical Drawing

Reproducing Drawings

Graphs

Maps and Civil Engineering

Architectural

Tables

Learning to Read Working Drawings

Introduction

Time would be wasted in explaining to a worker the shape and size of an article and how it is to be constructed. A working drawing accurately gives all the information needed to make a project. It shows with a few lines, symbols, and notes what would take considerable time to fully describe. It would be difficult to remember an oral explanation and bothersome to look up details of construction in several pages of written directions.

This book will provide instruction in making simple working drawings, house plans, layouts, maps, charts, diagrams, and how to obtain the information required to make an article from such a working drawing.

In working drawings, as in any written language, ideas are expressed graphically by a combination of views and symbols. These graphic expressions form the world language of architecture and engineering. The views and symbols used on working drawings can be understood in practically all parts of the world. Working drawings, diagrams, maps, graphs, and many similar drawings appear in books, magazines, and catalogs to aid in an understanding of the printed information. A designer makes many calculations to determine proportions and sizes and even form, the results of which would be impossible to remember. The working drawing serves as a language to express and record ideas.

Pictures

In many magazines, hobby books, and catalogs, objects are shown by line drawings in pictorial form. The pictures illustrate and supplement the explanations and give a better idea as to the appearance of the object. They save time and many words of explanation. Drawings in any pictorial form represent objects as they appear to the eye from one viewpoint. Even with familiar objects, surfaces seem out of shape; the relation of one part to another and the relative sizes are confusing. Much time is spent in reading the explanation and trying to find the needed information.

Working Drawings

To make an object as required, the worker must have a clear representation of the shape and definite, accurate information about the size, details, special processes, materials, and finish. In a pictorial drawing, it is difficult to satisfactorily furnish the information needed. Drawings with two or more views are used to accurately show the shape and give complete information about the size, materials, and finish needed. Such working drawings meet all requirements and avoid much confusion.

For each of thousands of manufactured articles — tools, machines, buildings, electric and gas lines, to name a few — designs are produced by designers and engineers. Final drawings are made by draftsmen. The millions of manufacturers, contractors, and workers find it necessary to use the drawings so painstakingly prepared. One can easily understand what an important place the working drawing holds in the industrial world. The making and reading of working drawings are of first importance in the present scheme of production and sales.

Homeowners and contractors, engineers, lawyers, doctors, dentists, skilled mechanics, and many others need to know how to read working drawings. The drawings that all these people have occasion to use, although not alike in many ways, are made on the same principles. It is a challenge to read and interpret accurately a working drawing, whether it be in the school or in the home workshop.

When we talk about *reading a drawing* or *reading a blueprint,* we mean that we seek information about how to produce the object. Blueprints are made from original drawings and often we say *read the blueprint* when actually the prints of original drawings may be in black and white or brown and white, as well as blue and white. Years ago the first permanent prints from the original drawings were blue, hence the expression *read the blueprint,* and we still often say it that way regardless of the color of the print.

With a little effort, one can learn to read working drawings with two or more views. With a knowledge of a few basic principles common to drafting and the symbols peculiar to a given field, one can learn to read machine, architectural, structural steel, concrete, railway, electronic, sheet metal, and several other types of working drawings. By referring to handbooks, one may learn the symbols of a particular field much in the same way as one would come to understand the meaning of a word in a dictionary.

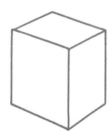

Fig. 1. Block

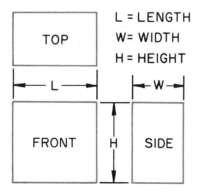

L = LENGTH
W= WIDTH
H = HEIGHT

Fig. 2. The Three Views of an Orthographic Projection

Two-view drawings are common. Many drawings have three views. The arrangement of the views follows a definite, standard system.

Figure 1 is a picture of a block. In Fig. 2, the same block is shown in three views. This is referred to as an *orthographic projection.* Each view shows a surface of the block as it appears from a point directly in front of that surface.

1. Looking down squarely at the top from a point above, you see the true rectangular-shaped *top view.*
2. Looking squarely from a point in front, you see the rectangular *front view.*
3. The *side view* is as seen looking squarely from the right side.

The front view is directly below the top view, and the side view is directly at the right of the front view. This is the standard arrangement of orthographic projections. If only two views are shown, they may be the top and the front or the front and the side. The views are drawn in the same relative position in a two-view drawing as in a three-view drawing.

In Fig. 2, observe that the length of the top view and the length of the front view are the same. Also observe that the height of the front view and the height of the side view are the same. Observe that the depth of the top view from front to back is the same as the width of the side view.

Questions

Directions for all questions in this book: Use a sheet of paper to record your answers. Do not write in the book. Your teacher may ask you for the answers orally instead of writing them because these questions are to help you in study rather than to test you.

The true-false statements are answered in the same manner as true-false statements that you have used in tests. On your paper, write the number of the statement and write the letter *T* or *F* after it. For example, the first statement is true; therefore, write *1-T* on your paper.

The statements with the capital letters enclosed in parentheses ( ) are completion statements. On your paper, write the number of the statement, the letter, and the correct word. For example, an-

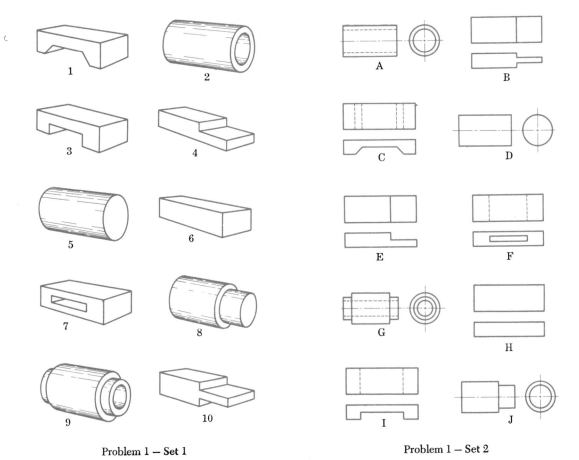

Problem 1 — Set 1

Problem 1 — Set 2

swer statement *3* as follows: *3A* architect, *3B* engineer.

1. A working drawing shows on one sheet what would require a long time to explain in words. (True or False)
2. In a working drawing (A) are used to express ideas.
3. The language of the working drawing is world language of the (A) and the (B).
4. The working drawing is an (A) and a (B) of an engineer's ideas.
5. Usually working drawings, like a photograph, have one view. (True or False)
6. A side view is placed directly below the top view. (True or False)
7. The *length* of the top view and the *width* of the side view are the same. (True or False)

Problem 1

Study the drawings in Sets *1* and *2*. Set *1* shows pictorial drawings; Set *2* shows two-view drawings of the same objects. Each pictorial drawing is numbered and the two-view drawings in Set *2* are indicated by a letter. On your paper, write the number of each pictorial view followed by the letter indicating the corresponding two-view drawing of the same object. For example, drawing *1* matches *C* in Set *2*. You should write *1-C*.

Lines of a Drawing

In viewing objects, some outlines are *visible* and others are *hidden*. In drawings, *visible outlines* are shown by dark, heavy lines known as visible outlines. *Hidden outlines* are shown by broken lines consisting of short dashes. These are

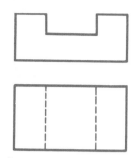

Fig. 3.   Drawing with Hidden Outline

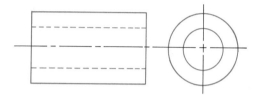

Fig. 4.   Use of Center Line

called *hidden* or *invisible outlines*. The sides of a groove cut in the bottom of a rectangular block would appear as broken lines of short dashes in the top view. See Fig. 3.

The *axis* (line of center) of any symmetrical part is shown in all views by center lines, consisting of fine long and short dashes. Observe that the *center line* in the front view, Fig. 4, indicates the *axis*, and that the intersection of the two center lines in the end view designates the *exact center* or *axis* of the circular view of the cylinder. All circular views require two center lines.

Questions

Directions: Follow directions for the foregoing statements.

8. In Set *2* of the problems, which three objects have holes through them?
9. Object *J* is hollow. (True or False)
10. The center of the side view in *D* is indicated by the crossing of a perpendicular and a horizontal (A).
11. *G* is the same diameter throughout its entire length. (True or False)

12. The square surface of the top view in *E* is lower than the rectangular surface at the left. (True or False)

Dimensions

The views show the shape of an object and the relation of its parts but do not give the exact size. In a complete working drawing the size is shown by dimensions. See problems 2, 3, and 4.

Certain kinds of lines are used with dimension figures to accurately express size. *Fine extension lines* extend from the limits of the distance that is measured. These lines are separated from the object by a very short space. The *dimension line* extends between the two extension lines, has an *arrowhead* at each outer end at the extension line, and a break near the center for the dimension figure, indicating the size.

The sign ′ indicates *feet;* the sign ″, *inches.* Fifteen feet is shown 15′; ten inches is shown 10″; fifteen feet, ten inches would be 15′-10″. When all dimensions are in inches, the inch marks may be omitted. *Degrees* are indicated by a small circle at the upper right of the number, thus 45°. A *minute*, 1/60 of a degree, is represented by the same mark as for a foot.

Notes

The size of a small hole, a chamfer, or some other detail of construction is often shown by a note a little removed from the view. A fine unbroken line with an arrowhead *leads* or refers to the part dimensioned. This is a *leader* and it should be placed at an angle so it will not be confused with dimension lines. Leaders also are used with notes about finish, fastenings, operations, and the like, as shown in problem 4.

Some of the more common notes are for such operations as drill, bore, and chamfer. Abbreviations are often used:

¼ Drill (DR)
¾ Bore
⅛ x 45° Chamfer (CHAM)
Finish All Over (FAO)
Material: Galvanized Iron (GI).

Several hundred such abbreviations exist for engineers, architects, and draftsmen. They may be found in handbooks such as listed on page 249.

Scale

Many objects are too large to be drawn full-size on paper; therefore the drawing must be small enough to be placed on a sheet of paper of convenient size, but with all parts in exact proportion. See problems 2, 3, and 4. The drawings of small objects often are made larger than the object. When drawings are made smaller or larger than the object, they are said to be drawn to scale. Generally, the scale is given in the title or in the form of a note on the drawing.

Drawings made to full-size are exactly the same size as the object. Drawings also are made to half-scale; that is, measurements on the drawing are made one-half the actual dimensions of the object. Similarly, drawings are made to quarter scale and to double scale. Drawings of buildings and other structures are made to small scale: so many inches to the foot, as ¼, ⅛, 1½, and other scaled proportions. The scale to which a drawing is made is indicated thus — Scale: Half-size; Scale: ¼″ = 1′-0″.

Many persons have need not only to read working drawings and diagrams, but also to make drawings to help in planning and to give another person an accurate idea of what is desired, such as a mechanical device, construction detail, or a diagram of data.

Preparations for a Drawing

In the units that follow, you will be given instruction in making working drawings, Units 2-7; in dimensioning such a drawing, Unit 8; and the making of dimension figures and lettering notes and titles, Units 9-13. Finally, instruction is given in making a working drawing with instruments.

Questions

13. The dimension line is fine and has a (A) near the (B) for (C) figure.
14. When a drawing is made to scale it is either (A) or (B) than the actual object.

Problem 2: Link

1. What is the radius at the large end of the link?

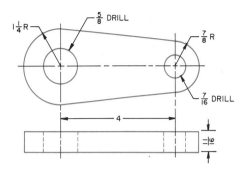

Problem 2 — Link

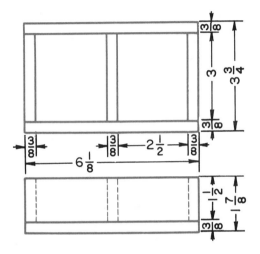

Problem 3 — Nail Box

2. How are the holes made in the ends?
3. The link is thicker at one end than at the other. (True or False)
4. The hidden edge lines show that the piece is symmetrical. (True or False)

Problem 3: Nail Box

1. Make a list of finished pieces for the parts of the nail box. List the number of pieces, the name and the size of each.

Problem 4: Steam Chest Cover

1. How many holes are there?
2. How deep is the depression in the bottom of the steam chest cover?

3. What is the diameter and the height of the pad on the top?

4. How is the upper part of the side view shown? (See 9 in Unit 5.)

5. What is the distance between the holes on the side?

6. What is the thickness of the steam cover? How are the ⅝″ holes made?

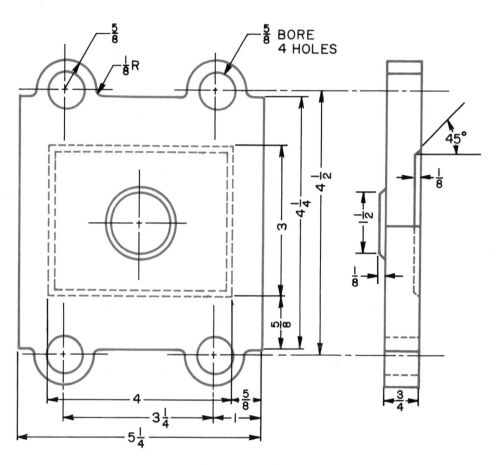

Problem 4 — Steam Chest Cover

Selecting and Sharpening a Drawing Pencil

The pencil is one of the most important instruments that you will use in drawing and in lettering. It must be properly selected for the kind of work to be done and the kind of paper on which it is to be used. To obtain best results, it must be sharpened properly for sketching, lettering, or use with a straightedge.

Selecting the Pencil

When working on mechanical drawing paper, use a hard pencil. On common writing paper, use a medium soft pencil. On art paper a soft pencil is best. It is important to keep in mind when selecting a pencil to choose one that is not too soft for the paper. Pencil lines, in any drawing, must be made so that the lines will, for a long time, remain as clear as when first made. For example, a common pencil used on a good grade of mechanical drawing paper will make lines that will smear and look dirty. However, a pencil that is too hard is difficult to use when sketching or lettering on drawing paper. Freedom of movement is not permitted because the hard lead follows the rough grain of the paper.

In order to make possible the choice of a pencil for a particular purpose, letters are printed on each pencil at one end. This letter indicates the degree of hardness or grade, Fig. 5. Pencils marked with *B* are soft, those marked *HB* and *F* are medium soft, and those marked with *H* are hard. If a number appears before a letter, as for example, *2B* or *2H*, it means that the lead is softer or harder according to the number and letter. Pencils are graded from *6B*, very soft, which are used by artists to *9H*, very hard, which are used by stone cutters. There are about seventeen grades of pencils for use in special kinds of work in various occupations.

In making mechanical drawings, *H* to *4H* and even *6H* pencils are used. The grade will vary according to the paper and the grading of the manufacturer. For sketching, an *H* or a *2H* pencil may be used. Penciled tracings usually are made with grade *2H* or *3H* pencils.

Whatever kind of drawing or lettering that you do, in order to do neat work, it is important that the pencil be sharpened correctly and kept properly sharpened. Examine your pencil frequently to see that it is in proper condition. A pencil used in making straight lines with the aid of a straightedge must be perfectly sharp. A light or white spot on the tip means that pointing is necessary.

The point of a pencil used in sketching may be slightly rounded. To get best results, hold the pencil rather lightly, two or three inches from the point.

Sharpening the Pencil

To make lines in mechanical drawing there are two kinds of pencil points that may be used; namely, the conical point and the wedge-shaped chisel point as shown in Fig. 6. For practical pur-

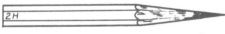

Fig. 5. The Letter Indicates the Grade

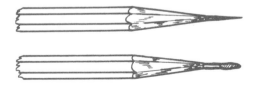

Fig. 6. Conical Point — Flat Point

poses and for all-around work the point in the shape of a cone is most popular. By rolling the pencil between the fingers while drawing a line, the conical point remains in good condition longer than otherwise. The chisel point is believed by some draftsmen to remain sharp longer than the conical point. Others like the chisel point for straight line work.

Some drafting rooms have special mechanical pencil sharpeners to remove the wood and save the time of the draftsman. However, the knife and a small sandpaper board pointer, Fig. 8, will be satisfactory. A small fine file may also serve, but it must be cleaned each time it is used. The layer of sandpaper on the board-type pointer may be replaced periodically. Do not keep the pencil sharpening equipment on the drawing board, on the table, or near the instruments, since this will result in graphite smears on your drawings.

Fig. 7. Trim the Pencil so that ¼″ or more
of Lead is Exposed

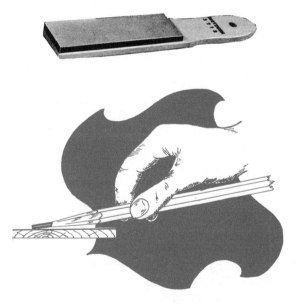

Fig. 8. Roll and Sharpen the Point on the
Sandpaper Pad

Conical Point

1. Sharpen the end of the pencil opposite the lettering so the identification of the grade of the pencil will be retained.

2. Hold the pencil in the left hand between the thumb and first finger. Hold the knife in the right hand. Place the end of the pencil to be sharpened between the thumb of the right hand and the blade of the knife. See Fig. 7

3. Remove the wood with a slicing cut, *but do not cut the lead*. Uncover ¼″ or more of the lead as shown in Fig. 7.

4. Dress the lead to a conical point, Fig. 6, by rolling the pencil between the fingers on a fine file or sandpaper pad, Fig. 8.

5. Wipe the pencil and lay the sharpener away in its place so it will not smudge the drawing or drawing tools.

Chisel Point

1. Dress the point on sandpaper or a file partly as in making a conical point, but complete the shape by holding the pencil flat on opposite sides until a wedge shape is obtained.

Questions

1. The pencil should not be sharpened on the lettered end because the letter helps in selecting the proper pencil after all the pencils have been sharpened. (True or False)

2. If one cuts the lead with a knife, the lead, being brittle, is quite likely to break. (True or False)

3. A fine grade of sandpaper should be used for sharpening. (True or False)

4. Why sharpen the pencil away from your drawing?

5. Why not use a common pencil sharpener for pointing mechanical drawing pencils?

6. Soft pencils are lettered with (A), and a number and hard pencils are lettered with (B) and a number on the end, and both are marked with the manufacturer's name.

7. Pencils used in mechanical drawing are (A), and those used in art sketching are (B).

Erasing

A firm pencil eraser of good quality is used in erasing pencil and ink marks. Patience is necessary when erasing ink lines. When good paper is used, an ink line or ink spot can readily be reinked after erasing provided the ink has been properly erased and the surface pressed down with a smooth, hard, curved object.

Erasing Pencil Lines

1. Be sure to use light pencil lines until you are certain that your work is correct.
2. Remove the instruments from the board.
3. Clean the eraser before using it by rubbing it on a piece of wastepaper.
4. Hold the thumb and forefinger of one hand in such position, near the area to be erased, that the drawing will not be torn or wrinkled while erasing with the other.
5. If it is necessary to protect adjoining lines, use the erasing shield, Fig. 9. Select the opening in the erasing shield that best fits the portion of the line to be erased. Hold the shield firmly in place over the line and proceed to erase through the opening. If you do not have an erasing shield, protect the adjoining lines with a piece of stiff paper.
6. With a dust brush, sweep the whole drawing board free of all particles.

Erasing Ink Lines

1. Follow steps, 2, 3, and 4 above.
2. If the ink is still wet, spread it with your finger and then let it dry for a few minutes.
3. Slide a triangle under the surface to be erased.
4. Select an opening in the shield that best fits the area to be erased, Fig. 9. Hold the shield firmly in place and proceed to erase through the opening.
5. Clean the surface with a brush and continue to draw.

Questions

1. If the hand, instead of a brush, is used for cleaning off particles left from erasing, the paper will become dirty. The dirt covering the particles of rubber is forced into the paper with the stroke of the hand. (True or False)
2. An ink eraser will destroy the smooth surface of the paper even through it erases the line quickly. (True or False)
3. An inked line to be erased should be blotted first. (True or False)
4. Why spread the wet ink before erasing it?

Fig. 9. Use Shield to Erase

Sketching Straight Lines

Fig. 10. A Conical Point, but not too Sharp

Fig. 11. Hold the Pencil Lightly, About Two Inches
from the Point

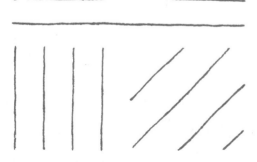

Fig. 12. Sketched Lines

Sketching is the making of straight lines, arcs, and curves free-hand and putting them together in various ways to express ideas. When planning a piece of furniture, a house, an automobile, or almost any object, an ability to sketch is of great advantage. Even doctors, dentists, lawyers, teachers, and salespeople find that sketching is very useful in explaining ideas to others quickly and clearly. An ability to make a simple sketch is of value to anyone.

The designer may express his ideas and make changes in a sketch more easily than in a drawing made with instruments. He studies outlines, relationships, proportions, and problems of layout and construction. By means of sketches, designers and engineers make their ideas clear to draftsmen and others. To be of value as a means of quick expression, sketches must be made entirely free-hand.

You should learn to sketch with skill, understanding, and confidence. Just as designers and engineers find the sketch of great assistance in their work, you will find that sketching is necessary before making the more accurate mechanical drawing.

By means of sketches, most difficulties in drawing and construction are met and overcome. Mistakes may be found and corrected before it is too late. In shop classes, you will find that sketches are useful in giving your teacher a clear idea of a project that you wish to make and for which there is no drawing. Ability to sketch will help you in many other ways in school and at home.

Sketching is not difficult if one follows certain principles that help to simplify it. But, of course, practice is necessary in order to make the right movements habitual, so you will not have to decide how to make each line and curve any more than you have to decide when to turn the front wheel of a bicycle to keep from falling.

1. To sketch a good line, see that the pencil is kept sharpened to a long, cone-shaped point, but not too sharp, Fig. 10.

2. Hold the pencil lightly, two inches or more from the point, as in Fig. 11. Make neat, sketchy lines consisting of a series of short, soft, light strokes, Fig. 12. Each stroke should just touch or even lap back a short distance over the one just made. In this way, a line may be drawn as long as is necessary and be kept fairly straight.

3. Lightly locate the points between which the straight line is to be drawn, Fig. 13. Starting at one point and keeping the eye on the other, sketch the line in successive strokes. If the line is not straight on the first attempt, erase that portion which may be wavy or uncertain and resketch to make it straight.

4. Use the eraser as little as possible to avoid smears and improve your control.

5. Sketch horizontal lines from left to right; vertical lines from the top downward, Figs. 14 and 15. In general, lines at a slant also are sketched in the same direction — from the top downward.

6. Practice sketching a line so you can make it in the desired form on the first attempt. Remember that the line should appear continuous, soft, and sketchy but certain.

7. When possible, keep the lower edge of the paper horizontal.

8. You can keep the pencil point from becoming flat if you will occasionally rotate the pencil in your fingers as you sketch.

Fig. 14.   Sketch Vertical Lines from the Top Downward

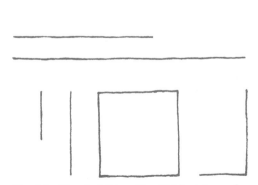

Fig. 13.   Sketched Lines Should Meet Squarely

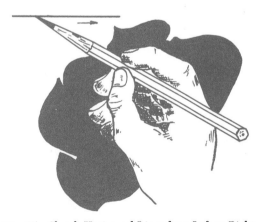

Fig. 15.   Sketch Horizontal Lines from Left to Right

Conventional Lines
of a Working Drawing

The lines used in drafting have been agreed upon generally by engineers and draftsmen. The lines have been *conventionalized;* that is, they are standard. The lines are of three widths as shown in Figs. 16 to 22. The differences are shown better in ink than in pencil. However, it is necessary that the lines be made properly whether you are working with pencil or with ink.

Fig. 16.   Border Lines

Fig. 17.   Visible Object Lines

Fig. 18.   Hidden Object Lines

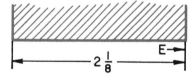

Fig. 19.   Dimension and Extension Lines

Fig. 20.   Center Line

Fig. 21.   Construction Line

Fig. 22.   Cutting Plane or Section Line

In Fig. 23 the lines are shown in a working drawing.

1. Make the *border lines* heavy when inking. They should be heavier than any of the lines. When drawn in ink a little less than $\frac{1}{32}''$ is not considered too wide by some draftsmen, Fig. 16. In penciling, a heavy black line is satisfactory.

2. *Visible outlines* of an object or part are represented by full, continuous, heavy lines. They stand out in strong contrast to all other lines. Be sure these lines are drawn exactly uniform in width and density throughout the drawing. In a penciled tracing or drawing, dense black visible outlines are required. To secure uniformity of lines on an inked drawing or tracing, carefully follow directions for inking. See Unit 59.

3. *Hidden outlines,* Fig. 18, are broken lines that represent edges and outlines hidden from view that must be shown but in contast with the visible outlines. Hidden outlines show the workman that there are other hidden parts or shapes that must be included in his plans for making the object. Hidden outlines consist of $\frac{1}{8}''$ dashes with $\frac{1}{64}''$ spaces between them and are kept uniform throughout the drawing. These outlines are medium in width. They are made dense black in a penciled tracing or drawing.

4. *Dimension lines,* Fig. 19, are fine, full lines with a break near the center for dimension figures. They are much finer than outlines. When making a penciled tracing or drawing, make the dimension lines fine and black. If the drawing is to be inked or traced in ink, keep the dimension lines fine and light. Dense black dimension lines are required on inked drawings.

5. *Extension lines, E* in Fig. 19 are the short lines that tell to which part of the object the dimension refers. They lead from a point about $\frac{1}{32}''$ from the view and extend about $\frac{1}{8}''$ beyond the arrowhead. Make them fine and of the same width as the dimension lines, G, Fig. 23.

6. *Center lines,* Fig. 20, locate the centers of circles and the axes of symmetrical parts. They are fine, broken lines composed of uniformly long, $\frac{3}{8}''$ or longer, dashes separated by uniformly short $\frac{1}{16}''$ dashes. The spaces between the long and the short dashes are $\frac{1}{16}''$. The length of the dashes and the spaces may be varied to the size of the drawing.

7. *Construction lines and projection lines* are used in blocking in views or otherwise making the first lines of a drawing in pencil, Fig. 21. Make them fine and light so they can be erased when necessary. Construction lines should be invisible at arm's length.

8. *Cutting plane lines* are used to show the imaginary plane of separation of an object which exposes the contour and internal area of a sectional view. The *sectional view* normally shows the area that cannot be seen in an orthographic or pictorial view, see *F* in Fig. 23. Make the cutting plane line, Figs. 22-23, by drawing a series of uniformly heavy,

black dashes each about $\frac{1}{2}''$ long separated by 2 short dashes $\frac{1}{16}''$ long, each separated by $\frac{1}{16}''$ spaces.

9. *Section lines,* often called *crosshatching,* are used to show the sectional view in contrast to the remainder of the drawing. Make the section lines fine, the same width as dimension lines, spaced $\frac{1}{16}''$ to $\frac{1}{8}$ inch apart,, even farther on larger drawings. *F* in Fig. 23 shows the standard conventional crosshatching for cast iron and is the usual form used for sections of one piece or where the material of the several parts is the same. Space the lines in all sections uniformly throughout the drawing, but learn to do it "by eye," without measuring.

Questions

1. The working drawing of the jig, Fig. 23, contains most of the conventional lines. Match the names of the lines shown in Figures 16 through 23, with the lines marked with letters in the drawing of the jig. Example: *V* and Fig. 17.

2. The line that shows where a measurement stops is a: (1) section line, (2) extension line, (3) parallel line, (4) visible outline, (5) heavy line.

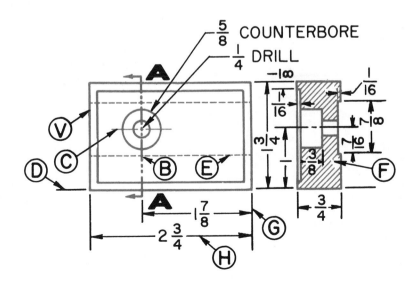

Fig. 23.   Jig

Selecting and Arranging Views for a Working Drawing

You have learned in reading working drawings that a common picture or a pictorial drawing ordinarily does not contain information for construction. A picture is taken from one position as it is seen with the two eyes, Fig. 24. All that can be seen with the two eyes from one position is shown. The exact shapes and sizes of the sides, top, and even of the front do not show in a photograph.

A working drawing shows the true shape of the object. The object is seen from one direction at a time and with one eye, Fig. 25. The shape of one face is called a *view*. As many views are made as are needed in order to obtain the exact shape and size of the object. The shape of the object determines, therefore, how many views are necessary. In Fig. 26 are shown three views of a vise liner block just as they would appear in a working drawing. You will observe that although three views of the block are shown, two would be sufficient. If two faces of an object are alike, they are shown only once.

The views of a working drawing are arranged in the proper relation to each other, as is shown in Fig. 26. In a drawing, it is necessary to leave enough space between the views to give the sizes or dimensions. There are certain principles to follow in choosing and arranging the views for an object to be drawn.

Relative Position of Views

1. Examine Fig. 27 and observe the shapes and arrangement of all views of the vise liner block.
2. The side or end view is placed exactly at the end or side of the front view. A left-side view or a right-side view or both may be needed; but in nearly all drawings the right side is shown when both views are alike. The top view is placed directly above the front view. There seldom is a bottom view, but if one is needed it is placed exactly below the front view.
3. Examine Fig. 27 more closely and observe that line *AB* in the top view is the same as the line *AB* in the side view. These lines must be drawn exactly the same length because line *AB* in the top view represents surface *X* in the side view. The object is the same all over in thickness; so line *DC* in the top view is the same length as line *AB*.

Fig. 24. Block, Pictorial Representation

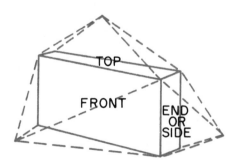

Fig. 25. Block as Viewed for Drawing

The lines with the same letter in Fig. 27 are the same in length because they are related to the same surfaces.

4. Study the object you are to draw in its position when in use and decide which is the front. If the object has no particular position when in use, the face that has the most descriptive shape should be chosen either for the front, the top view, or the side view.

5. Study the object with respect to the view at the right of the front view. Notice that the view at the side is exactly at the right of the front view. The top line of the side view is in line with the top line of the front view. The same is true of the bottom lines of the front view and the side view. Observe that the width or depth of the side view is the same as the depth, front to back, of the top view, Fig. 26.

6. After you have sketched the views, draw them with the instruments. Make all horizontal lines with the T square, carrying them across from one view to another at one setting, working from the view that has the most shape. Make all vertical lines with a triangle, carrying them from one view to another with one setting. When you are drawing lines from one view to another you are projecting them. One view is projected from another in this way.

7. Leave a space between views. so that the sizes can be indicated. This space is supposed to be the same between all views, but in practical work little attention is given to making the spaces equal because the placing of dimension lines between views has much to do with the amount of space allowed. Your assignment on dimensioning will tell you how much space to allow between views. If there are no dimensions, allow an inch between views and make the spaces equal.

Questions

1. In a working drawing the top view is placed exactly above the front view. (True or False)
2. The right side view of an object is placed at the left of the front view. (True or False)
3. A (A) does not contain the necessary (B) for making an object.
4. Why should the top view be placed directly above the front view?
5. What is the purpose of a working drawing?
6. Why should Fig. 25 need only two views if used in a working drawing?

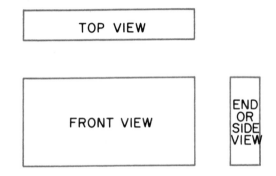

Fig. 26. Three-View Drawing of Block

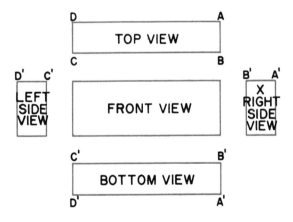

Fig. 27. Complete Representation of Oil Stone

Unit 7

Making a Simple Free-Hand Working Drawing

A free-hand sketch will be required for each problem before you make the instrument drawing. The sketch must be complete and give accurate information for making the instrument drawing, or even for making the object shown by the sketch.

The views are made complete and in the proper relation to each other. All parts of the sketch are made in proportion to all others. That is, a space two inches by four inches appears to be half as wide as it is long. A hole in the center of the space and one inch from the end is shown in the center and one-fourth of the total length from the end. Dimensions are complete and in correct form.

Making a Sketch Showing Top and Front Views

1. On an 8½″ x 11″ sheet of plain notebook paper, estimate the location of the sketch on the sheet.
2. Locate the ends of the two views and draw the vertical lines representing ends of the top and front views, Fig. 28.
3. On the vertical line at the left, Fig. 29, locate the lower edge of the front view at A.

4. Estimate the height of the front view at A. locate the upper edge of the view on the vertical line at B, Fig. 29.
5. Allowing one inch space between the views, locate the lower edge of the top view at C, Fig. 29, and also the upper edge at D, Fig. 29. Keep the distance across the top view from front to back in proportion to the height of the front view.
6. Through the points D, C, B, and A, starting at the top, lightly sketch the horizontal lines representing the upper and lower edges of the views, Fig. 30.
7. Darken the outlines, Fig. 31.
8. Sketch the extension and dimension lines, make the arrowheads, and letter the dimension figures, Fig. 32.

Making a Sketch Showing Front and Side Views

1. Estimate the location of the views on the sheet so as to have equal spaces outside the drawing at the top and bottom of the sheet. Allowing about an inch for dimensions at

Fig. 28. Locate and Draw the Ends of the Views

Fig. 29. Sketch the Upper and Lower Edges

the bottom, locate the lower edge of the front view at *A*, Fig. 33.

2. Locate the upper edge of the front view at *B*, Fig. 33.

3. Through *A* and *B*, Fig. 33, sketch horizontal lines extending them well toward the edge of the paper at the right.

4. Locate the left side of the front view at *A*, the right side at *D*, Fig. 34.

5. Allowing one inch between views locate the left and the right sides of the side view at *E* and *F*, Fig. 34.

6. Sketch vertical lines through points *A*, *D*, *E*, and *F*, Fig. 35.

7. Complete all details of the sketch and darken the outlines, Fig. 36. See Unit 5, steps 1, 2, 3, and 7.

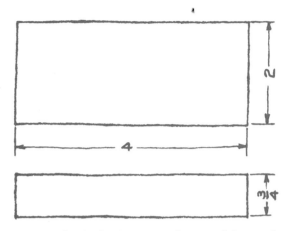

Fig. 32. Sketch the Dimension Lines and Letter the Dimension Figures

Fig. 30. Sketch the Upper and Lower Edges

Fig. 33. Locate the Lower and the Upper Edges of the Front View

Fig. 34. Locate the Ends of the Front View and the Sides of the End View

Fig. 31. Darken the Outlines

Fig. 35. Sketch the Vertical Lines

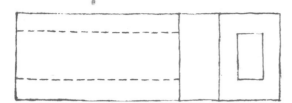

Fig. 36. Sketch all Details and Darken the Outlines

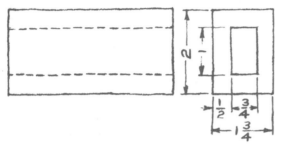

Fig. 37. Dimension the Sketch

8. Sketch the extension and dimension lines, make the arrowheads, and letter the dimension figures, Fig. 37. See Unit 5, steps 4 and 5; also Units 9, 10, and 11.

Making a Sketch Showing Top, Front, and Side Views

1. Estimate the location of the sketch on the sheet and *block in* (lightly sketch) the top and front views, extending the horizontal lines well toward the right of the sheet, Fig. 38.
2. Estimate the location of the side view, allowing an inch between the views. Sketch the vertical line, *EF*, Fig. 39, at the left of the side view, making it cross or intersect *AB*, the extended lower edge of the top view at *E*. See Fig. 39.

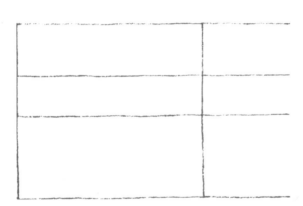

Fig. 38. Rough Layout of Sketch

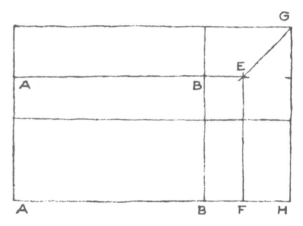

Fig. 40. Drawing Ready for Details

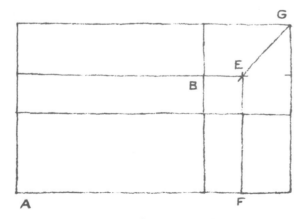

Fig. 39. End View Roughed In

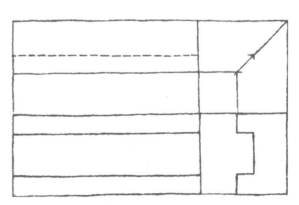

Fig. 41. Sketch Completed Except for Dimensioning

3. Through the intersection E draw the 45°
line, EG. Fig. 39.

4. Through G, draw the vertical line, GH,
Fig. 40, the right side of the side view. The
distance FH should equal BG in the top
view, Fig. 40.

5. The details of the drawing may now be
sketched, projecting points and lines from
the top to the side view or from the side
to the top view, Fig. 41.

6. Darken the outlines. Sketch the extension
and dimension lines, make the arrowheads,
and letter the dimension figures, Fig. 42.

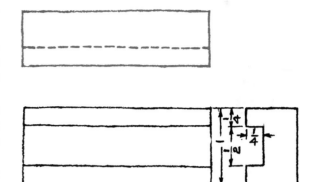

Fig. 42. Completed Sketch

Dimensioning
a Working Drawing

A working drawing shows size as well as shape. Indicating the size and location of various parts of the object on the drawing is called *dimensioning*. Without dimensions the skilled workman would be unable to proceed with the task of making the object. There are methods for dimensioning a working drawing that have been generally agreed upon; they have been conventionalized. These accepted methods of dimensioning a drawing have been determined by experience to be best for clearness and for preventing confusion and mistakes by the workman in making the desired object.

A drawing must also include information that clarifies the production requirements as well as size and location of parts. In metal manufacture, for example, the kind of surface and the required precision in machining and mating parts must be presented in the drawing. Dimensioning includes any special information necessary for precise work, and it is usually abbreviated or coded. Finish marks are shown in Fig. 47 as a V.

Drawing with Straight Lines

1. Size is given by dimension figures and lines, as shown in Fig. 43.

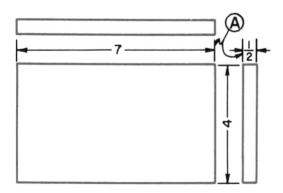

Fig. 43. Size is Given by Dimension Figures and Lines

2. After blocking in the views, make the extension lines hairlike but distinct. Start each extension line $\frac{1}{32}''$ from the object line and make it long enough to extend $\frac{1}{8}''$ beyond the dimension lines when drawn.

3. Place dimension lines $\frac{1}{4}''$ or more from the object. If there is more than one dimension, place them $\frac{1}{4}''$ apart as in Figs. 44 and 45. Uniform placing of dimension lines not only makes the drawing look better, but it makes it more convenient to read.

4. With a fine hairline draw each dimension line so it starts and stops exactly at the extension line. Leave an opening of about a half inch near the middle of the line for placing the dimension figure.

5. Make neat arrowheads at each end of a dimension line, placing them so the points are exactly at the extension lines. Fig. 43. Study and follow Unit 5, steps 5 and 6.

6. Make the figures for the whole numbers $\frac{1}{8}''$ high. Fractions are $1\frac{1}{2}$ times as high as the whole number. Make the dividing line of fraction in line with the dimension line.

   Some industries favor keeping the fractional line horizontal in all dimensions of diameters and radii. See Fig. 46. Such differences in local practice can be modified on the job.

7. Give the figure representing the full size of the finished object even though the drawing has been made to scale.

8. Place the dimensions and detail information on the drawing so they read easily. The figures should read from either the bottom or the right side of the drawing. If all figures can be read from the lower right corner, they are placed well, Figs. 43, 44 and 45. Many industrial drafting rooms require that all dimensions be placed so they may be read

from the bottom of the drawing as shown in the circle marked "preferred" in Fig. 46.

9. Give foot and inches as: 0'-0". In architecture, the foot and inch marks are used when a dimension is over 12". When all dimensions are in inches, the inch marks need not be used. In many metal industries, dimensions up to and including 72" are usually expressed in inches.

10. Dimension the thickness, width, and length of the object and any of its parts, Fig. 43, 44, and 45. Dimension the location of holes and other features.

11. Keep dimensions off the object whenever possible. Sometimes this cannot be done, as is shown in Fig. 45, but the more you can keep dimensions and notes off the views, the clearer the views will stand out and the fewer the chances for confusion.

12. Place dimensions between views whenever two views can be dimensioned with one line. This helps to make the drawing clear. See Figs. 43 and 44.

13. Give a dimension of a given feature but once, even though that part appears in another view. This is shown in Figs. 44 and 45.

14. Place the dimension near to the part it represents.

15. When there are several short and long dimensions together, as in Figs. 44 and 47A, place the short ones next to the view and the longer ones farther out.

16. When several dimensions are close together, place the figures so they are slightly to one side of each other, as in Figs. 44 and 47A. This is called *staggering*.

17. When a space is too small to place dimension lines between the extension lines, place short dimension lines outside of the extension lines. The figure can be placed inside the extension lines if there is enough space, or it can be outside of the extension lines if the space between is too small for a figure.

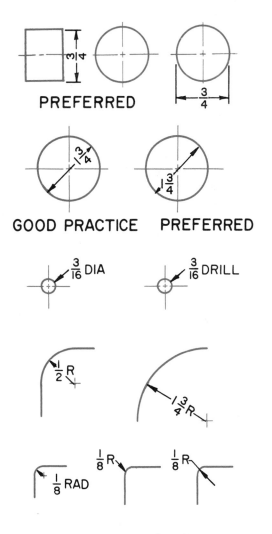

Fig. 46. Arcs and Circles

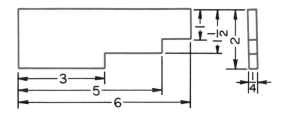

Fig. 44. Place Dimensions About ¼" Apart

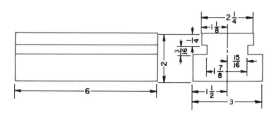

Fig. 45. All Figures Should Read from Lower Right Corner

See Figs. 44 and 45 for different treatments of narrow dimensional spaces.

18. When there are several dimensions in a row, or in a series, line them up as in Fig. 47A.
19. Group related dimensions.

Baseline Dimensioning

A finished surface from which measurements must be taken — a center line or a point that provides a fixed position for dimensioning — is referred to as *datum* or *baseline*. This term will have more reference as you advance in drafting. When there are two baselines as in Fig. 44, and one is vertical and the other is horizontal, they are said to be related to each other or *coordinate*. Baseline dimensioning is used to tie all dimensions to an exact plane, such as a finished surface or a center line.

Decimal System of Dimensioning

Many industries use the decimal system instead of fractions in dimensioning. It is believed that decimals simplify computations because decimals can be added, subtracted, multiplied, or divided more readily than fractions. Decimal equivalents of fractions appear in Table I.

In the decimal system, the inch is divided into *tenths*, as for example: .1, .2, .3, .4; and *hundredths* .01, .02, .03, .04, and so on. The second place decimal should be in even increments, as for example: .04, .06, .32, .68.

This method was originally adopted by the Ford Motor Company in 1932, and since then it has been accepted and used by many other industries. It is possible that most industrial drafting rooms may eventually use this method. Drawings for overseas manufacture are often dimensioned with both decimals and fractions.

There are variations in many drafting room practices; they cannot all be included in a single course in drafting. Essentially, the most commonly accepted standards are presented here. You will be required to adopt whatever local practice is followed. This is true also in dimensioning.

Table I
DECIMAL EQUIVALENTS
OF COMMON FRACTIONS

Fraction	Decimal		Fraction	Decimal
1/64	.01563		33/64	.51563
1/32	.03125		17/32	.53125
3/64	.04688		35/64	.54688
1/16	.0625		9/16	.5625
5/64	.07813		37/64	.57813
3/32	.09375		19/32	.59375
7/64	.10938		39/64	.60938
1/8	.125		5/8	.625
9/64	.14063		41/64	.64063
5/32	.15625		21/32	.65625
11/64	.17188		43/64	.67188
3/16	.1875		11/16	.6875
13/64	.20313		45/64	.70313
7/32	.21875		23/32	.71875
15/64	.23438		47/64	.73438
1/4	.250		3/4	.750
17/64	.26563		49/64	.76563
9/32	.28125		25/32	.78125
19/64	.29688		51/64	.79688
5/16	.3125		13/16	.8125
21/64	.32813		53/64	.82813
11/32	.34375		27/32	.84375
23/64	.35939		55/64	.85938
3/8	.375		7/8	.875
25/64	.39063		57/64	.89063
13/32	.40625		29/32	.90625
27/64	.42188		59/64	.92188
7/16	.4375		15/16	.9375
29/64	.45313		61/64	.95313
15/32	.46875		31/32	.96875
31/64	.48438		63/64	.98438
1/2	.500			

Drawings with Arcs and Circles

1. Study Fig. 46 and learn the accepted methods of dimensioning arcs and circles. Methods of dimensioning drawings that have straight lines also apply to drawings that have arcs and circles.

2. The center lines that are used for locating circles when drawing them are also used to locate the center for the workman. There must be center lines for every hole, circle, or symmetrical part.

3. Dimension the centers of all cylindrical holes from a center line, a finished surface, an important hole, or a base line such as a working edge, Fig. 47A.

4. Some metal industries require sizes of holes be indicated in decimals.

5. Dimension a circle by giving its diameter. Dimension an arc by giving its radius. Mark all radii with *R* or *RAD* as shown in Fig. 47A.

6. Center lines may serve as extension lines, but they must never be used as dimension lines.

7. Dimension the diameters of cylindrical forms between the views with extension lines drawn from the elevation, not from the circles. Place

the diameter of a location circle across the circle at an angle to avoid the center lines.

8. Do all adding or subtracting to make the drawing clear to the workman. The draftsman is responsible for all figuring and the workman makes the object. Add all detail dimensions and give the over-all dimension.

9. In many drafting rooms of industry, on drawings for parts produced in large quantities, it is required that only dimensions and notes for final forms and sizes be given. The method of manufacture is not noted. For example, the diameter of a hole is given without indicating on the drawing whether the hole is to be drilled, reamed, punched, or made in some other way.

Drawings in Precise Manufacture

Some metal objects in common use may have surfaces which have an unfinished foundry texture with areas on the object machine finished,

such as tools or machinery. The standard symbol for metal surfaces to be finished is a V-shaped 60° angle mark with the point touching the line representing the edge of the surface to be finished, as shown in Fig. 47B. If the piece is to be finished all over, the letters *FAO* are marked on the draw-

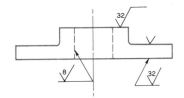

Fig. 47B. Symbols to Indicate Finish Surface

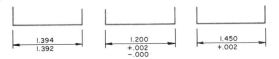

Fig. 47C. Methods of Indicating Tolerance in Dimensioning

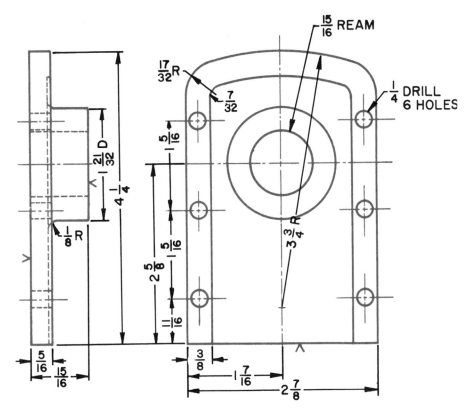

Fig. 47A. Dimension Holes from Center to Center by Extending Them from Finished Surface for Reference to Location
(Note Left Side View Shown)

ing. Certain metals (such as rolled stock which usually comes in sheets, rods, or square bars) have smooth surfaces and will not need finish marks in the drawing unless polishing and grinding are required.

In manufacture, there are varying degrees of surface smoothness that can be machined. Friction and wear to which the part will be subjected usually determine the amount of machining required. Aircraft, spacecraft, automobile, and electronics manufacturing must be especially exacting in the fitting of parts that are to be subjected to high speed, heavy loads, and heat. Friction and wear must be at a minimum. The quality of the metal, precision of fitting, and the finish of the surfaces must be included in the plans for manufacture. The symbols used to indicate the type of finish on the blueprints have been conventionalized by the United States of America Standards Institute (USAS). The USAS replaced the American Standards Association (ASA).

Sometimes the lowercase "f" is still used to designate *finish*, but the V-shaped mark is the standard symbol. If a surface is to be machined for appearance rather than for quality, the V-

shaped mark alone may be used, Fig. 47B. If a machined surface is to be finished, a symbol or code letter is added to the V-shaped mark to specify the quality of finish, Fig. 47B. Table II lists the qualities of surface and their code letters. Some manufacturers have their own code letters, but most manufacturers use the USAS.

The terms roughness, waviness, and lay identify the quality of a surface. *Roughness* refers to the usual smooth surface produced by machining without regard for the ultimate service to which it is subjected. There are small machine furrows or mill marks that may be observed and felt. The degree of roughness permitted is indicated by standard symbols. *Waviness* of a surface refers to the spacing of the furrows. *Lay* is the predominant pattern of the marks and their direction. They are measured in microscopic inches, usually .001 graduations. All the following terms will have greater meaning and you will use them as you advance in engineering design and drafting.

There are many other terms that have been standardized in engineering design. A few of these are fits, limits, tolerances, and allowances. Most terms that refer to precision allowance are related, and the dimension standards are similar.

When parts function together and when friction and wear must be as near zero as possible, *fit* is the term used to indicate the mating of such parts. There must be *limits*, or the maximum and minimum dimensions allowable. *Tolerance* is the amount of variation permitted in the fitting of close-functioning parts; it is the total plus and minus difference specified by the designers. *Allowance* is the intentional difference permitted in the precise matching of two parts that function together.

Allowance in dimensioning makes sure that all conditions are met relating to speed of the assembly of the parts as well as the service expected of the parts under conditions of wear and stress. When a mechanic produces a part, his skill can control the minimum and maximum accuracy required on a given part. However, when large numbers of parts are to be made, mass-production methods are utilized to save time and to maintain standards of accuracy. A machine can produce hundreds of parts accurately while only one person or a computer is required to control the operation.

Table II
SURFACE ROUGHNESS VALUES
(Expressed in Microinches)

Symbol M*	Decimal Equivalent	Type of Surface
250	.025	Obtained by turning, milling, boring.
63	.0063	Considered quite smooth to the touch.
32	.0032	Fine finish by grinding, honing.
16	.0016	Surfaces subject to friction such as bearings.
8	.0008	
4	.0004	Very fine finish by grinding, honing, lapping, buffing,
2	.0002	polishing. Used in fitting that must withstand all
1	.0001	conditions of surface friction.

*One thousand

A minimum and maximum limit must be determined for the fitting of mating parts. The lower and higher limits of dimensions are usually indicated in the thousandths-of-an-inch. Tables giving an allowance for various operations performed on production machines such as drilling, reaming, lathe turning of rough and finished surfaces, milling, planing, shaping, grinding, and cutting of threads are available in several engineering handbooks.

A general allowance of fit may be indicated in the record strip. However, if certain areas or surfaces are to be specified for tolerance of fit, the dimensions for those areas are marked with a minimum and maximum allowance for accuracy. In Fig. 47C examples of such dimensioning limits are shown. There are many conditions and applications which are determined by the engineers and have been conventionalized by the United States of America Standards Institute. Engineers and designers refer to the *standards* continuously. Standards will become more familiar to you in advance mechanical drafting.

Questions

1. A drawing can hardly be called a working drawing unless dimensions are given. (True or False)

2. In making dimension lines and extension lines, use a (A) *H* pencil.

3. The division line in a fraction need not be in line with the dimension line. (True or False)

4. Whole numbers are (A) high and fractions are (B) times as high.

5. Extension lines should continue (a) ½ inch, (b) ¼ inch, (c) ⅜ inch, (d) ⅛ inch beyond the arrowheads.

6. Place dimensions (A) views whenever possible.

7. Every working drawing must show (A) as well as (B).

8. What notes in Fig. 47A may be left out in some industries?

9. A surface to be machine finished is marked at the edge with a (A) and if all surfaces are to be finished, (B) is marked on the drawing.

10. List five terms used in referring to the quality of finish of a surface in manufacturing.

11. List three terms used in manufacturing when referring to the fitting of parts that function together.

12. What is meant by precise manufacture?

Unit 9

Making Arrowheads

Dimension lines should always have neat arrowheads at the ends. The arrowhead is small and it may seem unimportant, but it must be neatly made and properly placed. The drawing may be well drawn, but if the arrowheads are not neat the whole drawing will be unattractive. Arrowheads are easily made if a little time is given to practice.

1. Make arrowheads with a *2H* pencil.
2. Study the shape of the arrowhead and its size in Fig. 48. Note how the arrowhead is very slender and how the sides are graceful curves.
3. With one stroke of the pencil draw each of the two graceful curves so they come together at the point. Make the width a little less than half the length, Fig. 48.
4. Make the strokes in the directions shown by the arrows, as in Fig. 49.
5. Make all arrowheads the same size, even in large drawings, except when small space makes smaller arrowheads necessary.
6. See that all arrowheads touch the extension lines exactly, Fig. 50. They must not fall short or extend beyond the extension line.

Questions

1. Select from the arrowheads shown the one you think will be the best to use on your drawing.

2. On a small piece of paper of the same kind as that on which you are drawing, make several arrowheads until you have made one that you think is perfect. Show this to your instructor for his approval. Then make three more just exactly like it to see if you have good control.

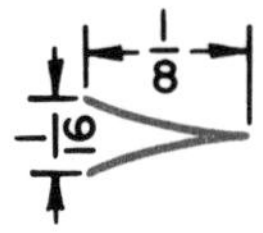

Fig. 48.   Enlarged Arrowhead

Fig. 49.   Steps in Making Arrowheads

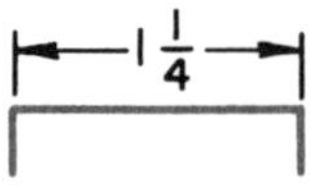

Fig. 50.   Arrowheads Touch Extension Lines

Forming
Letters and Numerals

A working drawing of any value has all the information regarding shape, relation of one part to another, the size of the whole and its parts, processes, finish, and material. The size is expressed in the form of dimension figures; the processes and materials are expressed in the form of lettered notes.

In drawing and in similar work, we speak of *lettering* the notes, charts, or posters rather than printing them because the characters are formed by hand in an orderly way and with care. Since the lettering is a necessary part of a drawing, it is essential that the lettering read easily. Lettering should be uniform in height, in width, and line weight.

A request to "please print" often appears when a form is to be completed. This is done in an attempt to make certain that names, addresses, and dates are read easily and without error. Lettering has many other applications — to titles, labels, notices, signs, posters, charts, maps, and so on.

Like any skill that you wish to acquire, lettering requires practice. If you have learned to play a violin, pitch a curve ball, or ride a bicycle, you know it takes practice. And you know that you must practice the right way. With a little determination, patience, and careful observation, you can learn to letter well.

The appearance of the lettering, including the numerals, on each drawing is a true measure of your ability in lettering. Each drawing offers an excellent opportunity to gain more experience in lettering.

The lettering used on working drawings is simple and consists of single strokes which are of uniform width. Throughout the drawing all letters and figures should be uniform in height; all like characters should be uniform in width and proportion.

Vertical lettering is most, generally used. It seems in harmony with the outlines of available space, which is ordinarily rectangular. Vertical lettering is widely used, and even required on working drawings in many industries.

After good habits of lettering are formed in vertical lettering, a reasonable skill can be acquired in slant lettering if required. The general form and proportion of the characters and the order of making the strokes are approximately the same.

Because all lines of the letters are of a single width, uniformly dark, and each is made with a single stroke, such single line lettering is called *single line Gothic*. A similar type face is in commercial use in printing shops.

Forming the Numerals and Letters

1. Sharpen a *2H* or a *3H* pencil to a long cone-shaped point, slightly rounding the very point.
2. On a piece of one-eighth inch cross-section paper, make an exact copy of Fig. 51. After carefully observing the proportion of a character, block out its width. Lightly sketch in the letter or figure, gradually bringing it to final form in a strong, clean, uniform line.

Picturing Numerals and Letters

To get a mental picture of the characters, examine the form and proportion of each in the accompanying examples and observe:

1. That the letters and numerals are composed of straight lines, ellipses, or a combination of these.

2. All characters are five units high. A space represents a unit.

3. Most of the letters are four units wide; *T, H,* and *U* are a little more than four units wide; *E, K, V, Y, C, G, O, Q, Z* and the numeral *0* are four and a half units; *M, A, X,* and the numeral *4* are five units, and *W,* eight.

4. Letters *E, X, K, Z, R,* and the numerals *8, 3, 2,* and *5* are wider at the bottom so they will not look top heavy but give a feeling of stability.

5. The characters are grouped according to similarity of shape.

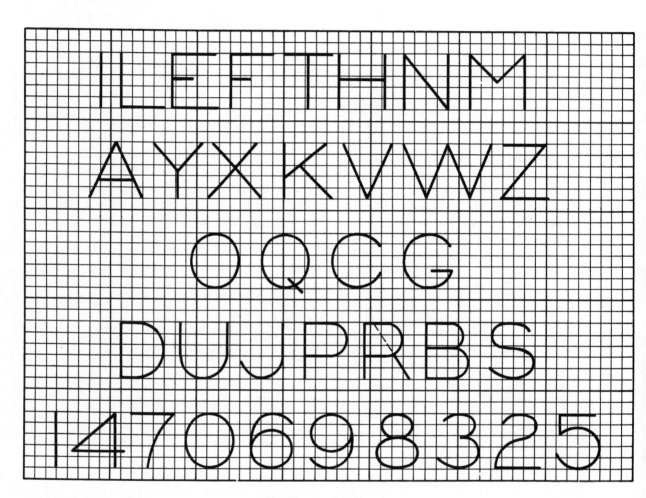

Fig. 51. Practice Exercise

Making Numerals

The dimension figures on working drawings are a very important part of the drawing. It is essential that the characters shall be plain, easily made and the kind used by engineers on drawings.

Follow the directions carefully. All the characters are five units (spaces) high. To be able to picture the completed character is of great help in keeping the right proportions and form.

Learn to form numerals and letters skillfully with as few strokes as possible, without lifting the pencil or pen. This saves time and is efficient. Be careful to make the corners sharp where required.

The following directions in this unit and in Unit 12 are especially for vertical lettering. They do apply in general, however, to the slant lettering, the construction of which is shown at the left in the illustrations.

Forming the Numerals

1. The numeral *1* is a single vertical stroke.

2. To form a *4*, first make the 45 degree stroke downward from right to left. Scarcely taking the pencil from the paper, make the horizontal stroke five units long from left to right. Make this stroke one third the height from the bottom. Complete the figure by making the vertical stroke from the top downward. When finished, the figure should look as wide as it is high.

3. To form a *7*, first make the horizontal stroke four units long. Complete the figure by making the second stroke downward. Notice that the bottom of the

second stroke is in the center and that the figure is balanced. The second stroke may be curved slightly as shown. To save time form the numeral in one continuous stroke.

4. To form a *0*, start a little to the right at the top and make a full rounded curve to the left downward and well up on the right. Finish the figure, starting at the top, with a full curve to the right and downward, joining the left half nicely at the bottom.

When completed, the figure should appear as a full ellipse, four and a half units wide, which is almost as wide as it is high. In extended lettering it will be a circle. Being able to form this figure easily will help you in forming the remaining ones.

5. To form a *6*, make a short curved stroke at the top and toward the right. Beginning again at the top, make the left half of an ellipse downward swinging well up on the right. Starting about a third of the way up on the inside of the curve and at the left, complete the ellipse which forms the lower part of the figure.

6. To form a *9*, first make the left side of the smaller ellipse at the top carrying the stroke well up on the right. Starting at the top of the curve already formed, make the curved stroke on the right,

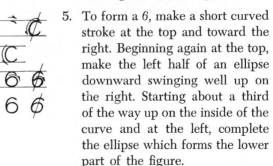

carrying it up and out slightly toward the left at the bottom.

7. To form an *8*, make the left half of the smaller ellipse at the top. Make the right half of the ellipse at the top. Make the left half of the larger ellipse at the bottom. Make the right half of the larger ellipse. The longer axis of each ellipse is horizontal. Keep the shorter axis of each in the same straight line. A small *8* may be formed by making each ellipse with one stroke, the upper one first.

8. To form a *3*, make the upper and the right portions of the upper partial ellipse. Form the right and lower portions of the lower partial ellipse. Observe that the first stroke starts inward a little straight, and that the lower is carried out in a similar way and a little farther than the upper part of the figure. In general, a *3* could be formed very nicely by making the two strokes as one without lifting the pencil. Observe the similarity between the *8* and the *3*.

In most drafting rooms, the flat top figure number three is not used because of the similarity to the figure five when it is inked.

9. To form a *2*, start just as in making the upper part of a *3*, continue as if to form the left side of the lower ellipse of an *8*, but carry the stroke downward to the bottom. Complete the figure by drawing the horizontal line to the right and making it a little more than four units long.

10. To form a *5*, make the upright stroke at the left by working downward two units. Form the full elliptical curve beginning at the lower end of the upright stroke and carrying it upward and out a half unit.

11. Fractions are made one and a half times as high as a whole number.

12. As a beginner you will be better able to make fractions in good form by making the horizontal division line first. In mechanical drawing this line is always in line with the dimension line.

13. Make the numerator, being careful to leave a small space between the bottom of the figure and the division line. The height of the numerator will be about two-thirds as high as a whole number.

14. Leaving a small space below the division line, make the denominator of the fraction. The height will be the same as the height of the numerator.

Practice the Numerals

1. On a 6″ x 9″ sheet (or similar size) of drawing paper (half of a regular problem sheet), rule fine, hairline lines lengthwise of the sheet and about ⅛″ apart. These lines will serve as guides for the tops and bottoms of of the numerals and should not be visible at arm's length. Similar guide lines are made for all lettering.

2. Make the first numeral, *1*, at the beginning of the first line. Be sure it is vertical, straight up and down.

3. Carefully observe the copy, estimate the location of the *4* on the line and form the numeral. Before actually making the character on the paper, you will find it of great help to go through the motions of forming the character by tracing the form with the pencil point, but without touching the paper. Also close the eyes and trace the form in the air.

4. Observe the form and proportion of *7*. Estimate its location in the line. Carefully form the numeral.

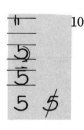

5. Compare your work with the copy, erasing and changing where it is necessary to make the characters the right form and proportion.

6. Have your work checked and get approval to continue the practice.

7. Complete the line, being careful to make like characters exactly alike. Make no differences whatsoever in shape or proportions.

8. Following the same procedure as in paragraphs, 1, 2, 3, and 4, locate and form the *0*

and the *6* in the second line. Have your work checked and approved. Complete the line. In a similar way study the *9* and the *8*, the *3* and the *2*, and the *5*, and also the fractions and mixed numbers, completing each line before starting the next.

9. When you have completed the sheet and it has been accepted, rule another with guide lines for numerals one-eighth inch high, and practice figures of that height. Dimension figures are usually one-eighth inch high.

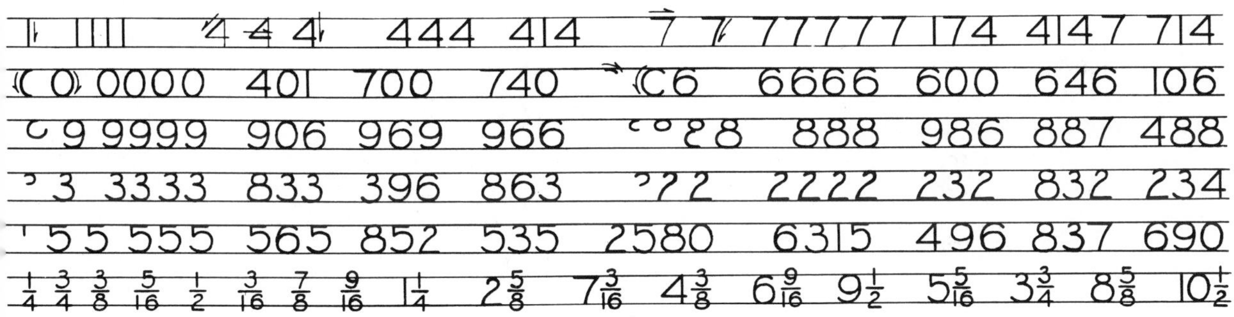

Fig. 52. Practice on Numerals

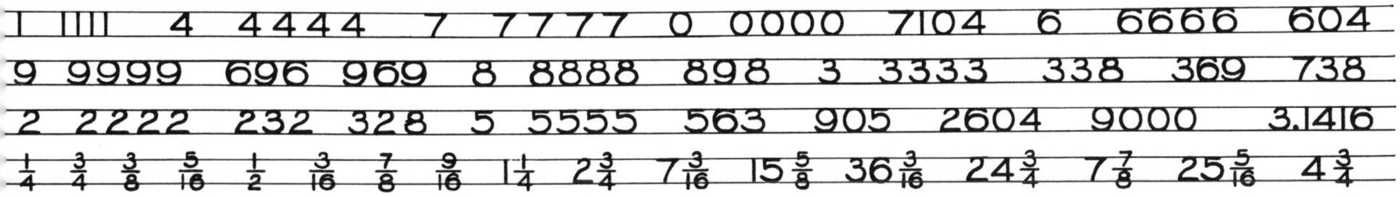

Fig. 53. Practice on Small Numerals

Making Small Letters

Titles and notes on mechanical drawings are exceedingly important. Title notations give necessary information regarding the name of the object, the scale, the date, and the name of the person by whom the drawing was made. Notes gives information regarding materials and processes. First, to make it certain that there can be no excuse for making a mistake in the product, the lettering must be easily read. Second, for appearance sake the lettering must be uniform. Third, the lettering must be easily done to save time and effort.

If you would learn to letter well, you must take time at the start to study the shape of each character and find in detail just how each one is made. You should take time to follow the directions exactly and to make the strokes in order. The same practice as used in making numerals should be carefully followed in lettering.

While learning to letter, avoid any lettering any place which you can not take time to do well. You must make it a rule to practice only the desired form and order of strokes.

The construction of each letter is described in detail in the following paragraphs.

An *I* is a single down stroke.

To make an *L*, first make the down stroke and then the horizontal stroke four units long.

To make an *E*, start with the down stroke, as in an *L*, then make the horizontal stroke four and one-half units long. Next make the horizontal stroke at the top four units long. To complete the letter make the middle horizontal stroke a little above the center and two and one-half units long. The longest stroke at the bottom gives a sense of stability to the letter.

To make an *F*, start with the down stroke, then make the horizontal stroke at the top. Complete the letter with the short stroke just a little above the center and two and one-half units long.

To make a *T*, first make the horizontal stroke at the top four units long. Starting exactly at the center of the horizontal stroke make the downward stroke. In an inclined letter *T*, start the slant line two and one-half units from the left end of the horizontal stroke.

To make an *H*, first make the vertical stroke at the left, second make the one at the right. The horizontal bar of the *H* is made about the width of the line above the center. This gives the letter the desirable appearance of stability.

To make an *N*, make the down stroke at the left, the diagonal from the top of the first stroke downward to the right, making it four units wide at the bottom. Complete the letter by making the down stroke at the right.

To make an *M*, first make the vertical strokes at the left and at the right just five units apart. Beginning at the top of the stroke at the left, make the half diagonal stroke toward the lower end of the stroke at the right. Finish the letter by making the half diagonal stroke from the upper

42

end of the stroke at the right toward the lower end of the vertical stroke at the left.

To make an A, first make the down stroke on the left, second the down stroke on the right. The width at the bottom is five units, the same as the height of the letter. The top must be exactly in the center and the two sides the same length. Complete the letter by making the horizontal stroke from left to right nearly a third of the height from the bottom. A line drawn through the apex at the top and the center of the base will form the axis of the letter.

In the inclined style of the letter, the down stroke at the right slants out only one-half unit.

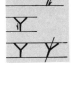

To make a Y, beginning at the right and top make the slanting stroke at 45 degrees, stopping at the center a little above half the height of the letter. Starting the second stroke at the top and four and one-half units to the right, join the first stroke at the center. The stem of the letter completes the character and forms its axis. The second stroke may be continued into the stem.

To make an X, make the diagonal stroke from the upper right to the lower left. Starting at the upper right four units from the first, make the second stroke, being careful to cross the first a little above the center. When finished, the letter must be four units wide at the top and four and one-half units at the bottom. It will be symmetrical with its axis.

To make a K, start with the down stroke on the left, then beginning at four units to the right, make the diagonal stroke downward, joining the first stroke two units from the bottom. Starting at the second stroke, two units from the top, complete the let-

ter by making the third stroke downward to a point four and one-half units from the bottom of the first stroke. Observe that the third stroke may be considered to spring from the top of the first stroke.

Also observe that in the slant letter the ends of the second and third strokes in the slant letter are in a vertical line.

To make a V, make the down stroke on the left to a point two and one-quarter units to the right. Starting at the top, four and one-half units to the right of the first stroke, make the second stroke downward joining the first at the bottom. This letter is symmetrical also.

In the inclined letter the stroke at the right slopes only one unit to the right; the axis passes through the center of the space at the top and the vertex of the V at the bottom.

To make a W, the process is a repetition of the V. However, each part is four units wide, making the whole letter eight units.

To make a Z, start with the horizontal bar at the top making the stroke left to right four units. At the right end of the first, make the diagonal stroke downward, right to left, one-half unit farther to the left than the left end of the bar at the top. Complete the letter by making the lower bar five units long. The letter can easily be made in one stroke. The character will then be four units wide at the top and five at the bottom.

To form an O, start at the top well over to the right and form the left half by continuing downward to the bottom and a little up on the right. Finish the letter by starting at the top and joining the curve at the bottom. When completed it should appear as an ellipse four and one-half units wide. A small sized *O* can be well made in one stroke.

The letter *Q* is formed in the same manner as an *O* except that a slanting 45 degree stroke from left to right is made one unit to the right of the axis. The elliptical part of a small sized *Q* can be made in one stroke.

To form a *C*, start at the top first and form a short curve downward on the right. Second, start at the top and form the curve on the left, bringing it well up on the right. The ending of the last curve may be rather straight.

With a little patience and care, one can learn to form a *C* and the elliptical part of a *G* with one continuous stroke and save time.

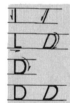

To form a *G*, follow the same process as for a *C* except that the horizontal bar is made from left to right two units from the bottom of the letter and is two units long.

To form a *D*, first make the down stroke at the left, going right into the lower horizontal stroke making it two units long, half the width of the letter. Beginning at the top of the first stroke, make the upper horizontal part of the stroke two units long and, continuing, form the elliptical portion of the letter just like the right side of an *O*.

To form a *U*, first make the down stroke at the left straight for about three and a half units. Continue halfway into the curve at the bottom. Make the second down stroke at the right just about four units from the first.

To form a *J*, make the straight down stroke three and a half units long, continuing half way into the curve at the bottom. To complete the letter, start at the left and form the curve, joining the first stroke nicely. When completed, the *J* is four units

wide. A small sized *J* can easily be formed with one stroke.

To form a *P*, make the down stroke, Then starting at the top of the first stroke, make the horizontal part of the second stroke three units long to the right, continuing into the formation of the curve and on into the horizontal straight line, joining it squarely a little below the middle. The letter when completed is four units wide.

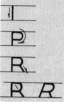

To form an *R*, make a down stroke. Then, as in a letter *P*, form the upper portion of the letter but three and a half units wide. The third and sloping stroke is started at the lower horizontal part of the loop two and one-half units to the right of the first stroke and is ended at the bottom four units from the first stroke. The inclined third stroke if extended to the top of the letter would strike one unit to the right of the first stroke.

To form a *B*, first make the down stroke. Second form the upper loop making it three and a half units wide and with the lower horizontal part of the loop joining the vertical stroke a little above the center. Form the lower loop, making it four units wide. The upper and lower loops can be continued as one stroke without lifting the pencil, especially in small sized letters. Care must be taken to make the straight part of the bars exactly horizontal. In *B*'s $\frac{3}{16}$″ and ¼″ high, it is a small advantage to continue the first stroke horizontally about two units. The lower loop, being larger, gives the letter the required appearance of stability.

Observe that the lower portion of the letter *S* is four units wide and that the upper loop is less in height than the lower.

To form an *S* higher than ⅛″, start at the top and make a short curve downward to the right. Again starting at the top form the upper loop to the left and continue to form the lower loop to the right, stopping just beyond the bottom. Complete the letter with a short downward stroke from the left, joining the lower loop smoothly at the bottom. This method works especially well with larger sized letters. The short strokes at the beginning and end of the curve often are the touches that make the appearance of the letter just right. This is particularly true in the case of an inclined S.

To form an S ⅛″ or less in height, start on the right at a point a unit down from the top. Form the upper loop, continuing through the center to form the lower loop to the right. Still continuing the stroke, complete the letter with an upward but slightly outward swing. This last part of the stroke will help make the letter appear wider at the bottom.

Practice the Letters

1. Rule two 6″ x 9″ sheets with guide lines ³⁄₁₆″ apart.

2. Observe the copy, Fig. 54, and estimate the location of the several letters in the first line. Make one *I*, one *L* and one each of the other letters in the order shown, making each one as nearly like the copy as possible. Be sure to leave enough space after each letter to finish the copy later.

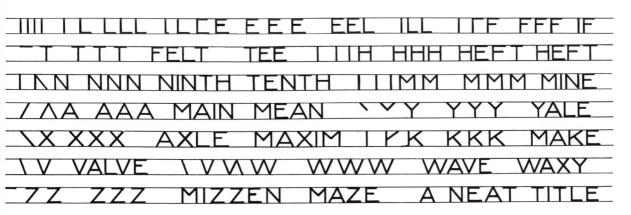

Fig. 54. Practice on Straight Line Letters

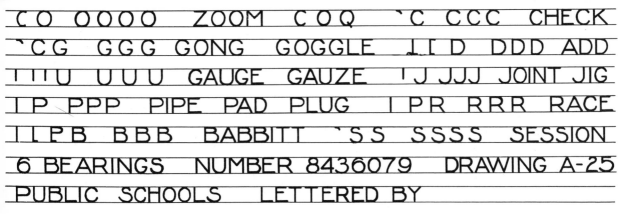

Fig. 55. Practice on Letters with Curved Lines

3. Compare your work with the model shown, erasing and changing where it is necessary to make the character conform to the model.

4. Have your work checked and get approval to continue the practice.

5. Complete the line, being careful to make like characters exactly alike. Make only such changes as will improve the shape or proportions and make it more nearly like the model.

6. With the same procedure as for the first line locate the position of the *T* and the *H* and form the letters. When your work has been checked and approved complete the line. Similarly proceed with each line until you have studied all the letters and completed all the lines. Likewise study and practice the letters in Fig. 55.

7. On the second sheet proceed in a similar manner with the letters that are elliptical or are composed of elliptical curves and straight lines. Fig. 55.

8. When you have completed the two sheets and your work has been accepted, rule two sheets with fine, light guide lines $\frac{3}{16}''$ apart. On one of these make a copy of Fig. 56. As a later assignment make a copy of Fig. 57.

Questions

1. Some letters are made wider at the bottom to give an appearance of (A).

2. What letter is similar to *E?* To *X?* To *V?* to *C?* To *U?*

3. What letters are similar to *Q?* To *R?*

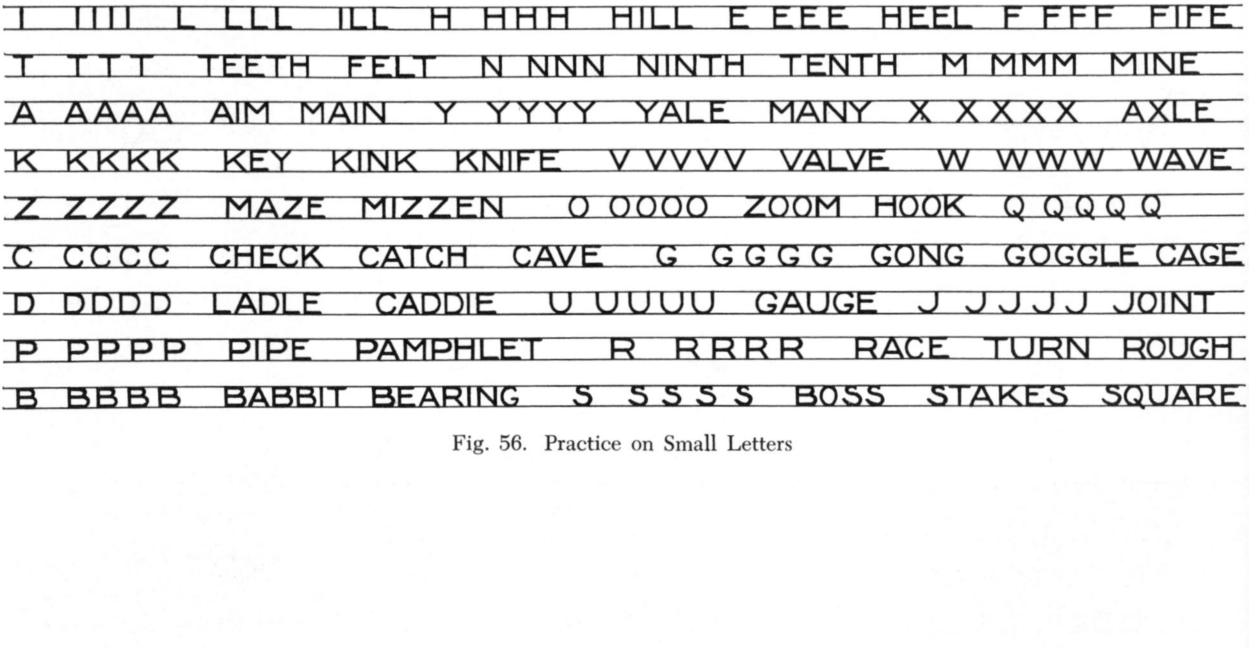

Fig. 56. Practice on Small Letters

Spacing Letters and Words in Composition

When you have learned to make the letters in the right form and in pleasing proportions, your attention should be given to joining the letters into words and the words into phrases and sentences. As in printing, this is called composition. The letters in a word must not be crowded together nor too widely separated. Either condition makes it difficult to recognize the word readily. To give a pleasing appearance and to make it easy for the eye to run along the words, the spaces between the letters should appear equal in area and a little less than the area within the letter.

To give the appearance of equal areas, the distance between the letters in the word *IN* should be greater than that between letters with curved sides such as *OG*. The horizontal tops of the two adjacent letters *TT* should have very little space between them while there should be no space between the letters in combinations, as *LT* or *AV;* the letters might even overlap. See Fig. 57.

Spacing really depends on the horizontal distance and the outlines of the adjacent sides of the letters. Spacing that gives a pleasing appearance to any composition of words or sentences and makes it easy to read, is considered more important than the formation of the letters. It is hard to follow set rules. However, a few general principles will be helpful.

Spacing Within the Word

For letters five units high, leave two units between such letters as *H* and *N* with adjacent sides having uniform direction. This gives a good standard for area between letters. In the word *NINTH*, Fig. 57, the space between the *N* and the *I* is two units. Because of the open character of the *T* the horizontal bar at the top is only half unit from the *N* on the one side and is the same distance from the *H* on the other side. The area between the letters appears to be nearly equal.

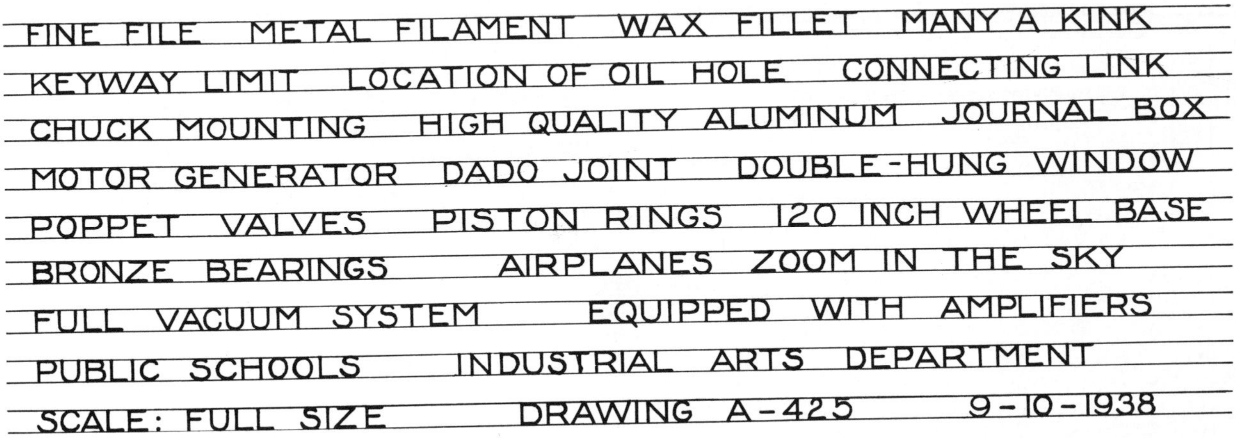

FINE FILE METAL FILAMENT WAX FILLET MANY A KINK
KEYWAY LIMIT LOCATION OF OIL HOLE CONNECTING LINK
CHUCK MOUNTING HIGH QUALITY ALUMINUM JOURNAL BOX
MOTOR GENERATOR DADO JOINT DOUBLE-HUNG WINDOW
POPPET VALVES PISTON RINGS 120 INCH WHEEL BASE
BRONZE BEARINGS AIRPLANES ZOOM IN THE SKY
FULL VACUUM SYSTEM EQUIPPED WITH AMPLIFIERS
PUBLIC SCHOOLS INDUSTRIAL ARTS DEPARTMENT
SCALE: FULL SIZE DRAWING A-425 9-10-1938

Fig. 57. Practice in Spacing Words and Letters

Spacing Between Words

A suitable space between words is equal to the height of the capital letters, or the space required for a standard letter such as *H* or *N*. To all appearances, the area of the spaces between words should seem equal.

Sentences

Twice the distance between words makes a proper space between sentences. A space equal to the letter M with proper space on the side could nicely be inserted between sentences.

Due to the room which is available for notes, the spaces between words may vary from line to line, but the spaces must be kept equal within the same line to allow the eye to follow the composition smoothly. The space between the letters in any composition is governed by any given combination of adjacent sides. This also may control the space between words and even between sentences.

Lines

When there are several lines or notes, the lines should be separated by equal distances. Such space may vary from one-half to one-and-a-half times the height of the letters. The exact distance chosen will depend on the available space and on the nature of the characters in the composition. A mixed number would make a greater distance necessary between all the lines than if only whole numbers were included in the note. For appearance the left side is kept straight; in long notes the right side is kept fairly so.

Numbers

The same general principles that apply to spacing letters also apply in combining numerals into numbers.

Again remember that the distinguishing characteristic of good lettering is its uniformity in height of letters, in width of lines, in direction of axes, in like characters, and in the shade, or color, of the composition which is due largely to careful spacing.

Practice Spacing

On a prepared sheet similar to Fig. 57, practice the spacing of letters and words, carefully observing the spacing as shown in the model.

Fastening Paper on the Drawing Board

There are a few operations in drawing that seem too simple for explanation. Fastening paper properly to the board is one of them. It is not simple, however, because a smooth, perfectly flat surface on which to draw is difficult to obtain unless a certain method is followed. To draw on paper that does not lie flat is very annoying.

1. Wipe the drawing board and T-square free of all dust.
2. When a sheet of drawing paper approximately 9″ x 12″ is to be used, place the sheet in the upper left portion of the drawing board — about six inches from the left edge and four or five inches below the upper edge of the board. With the paper in this area, you will have arm freedom; and the head of the T-square, being close at hand, can be readily kept firmly against the edge of the board.
3. Place the T-square in position with the head against the left edge of the board as at X, Fig. 58. Be sure the head is firmly against the edge of the board.

   NOTE: Instead of thumbtacks, many draftsmen prefer to use staples, drafting tape or some other device to hold the paper in place on the drawing board. In the following directions, *fasten* will mean to fix firmly in place with a thumbtack, staple, or a small ($\frac{1}{2}$″ x $\frac{3}{4}$″) piece of masking tape. Cellophane tape is too difficult to remove from the paper.
4. Fasten the upper-left corner of the paper.
5. With the head of the T-square held firmly against the edge of the board, adjust the upper edge of the paper to align with the upper edge of the T-square.
6. With one hand, hold the paper firmly in position; with the other hand, slide the T-square down toward the center of the sheet. Hold it firmly while changing hands to make one hand free.
7. With the palm of the hand, stroke the paper snugly to the board, working from A, the upper-left corner, to B, the lower-right corner, as shown by arrow E. Fasten at B. See Fig. 58.
8. Smooth the paper firmly toward the upper-right corner and fasten.
9. Test for correct adjustment with the T-square.
10. Stroke the paper (from the center) toward the lower-left corner and fasten.

Questions

1. Why wipe the instruments each time you prepare to work?
2. What is the advantage in carefully smoothing the paper before fastening it?
3. Why use masking tape in fastening rather than cellophane tape?

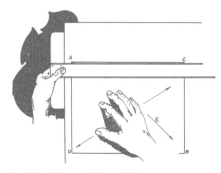

Fig. 58. The Upper Edge of the Paper is Parallel with the Edge of the T-Square

Drawing Instruments and Their Care

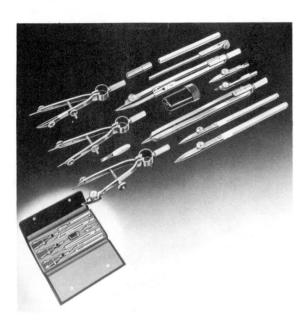

Fig. 59A. Set of Drafting Instruments

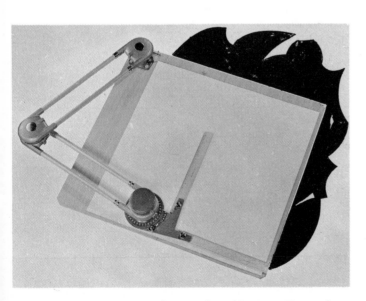

Fig. 59B. Drafting Machine (Courtesy, Universal Drafting Machine Corporation)

One of the first things a beginner in mechanical drawing has to learn is to appreciate and care for his drawing equipment and instruments. Every piece of equipment is made with the greatest care. The compasses, dividers, ruling pens, and bow instruments are made of nickel-silver and high-grade steel. Drawing instruments have finely fitted parts which makes it possible to adjust them for the most accurate work. They are precision instruments which are made for doing close accurate work and are comparable to a micrometer or to a watchmaker's instrument. They are placed in velvet-lined cases to protect them from injury, as are all fine instruments, Fig. 59.

Scales are made of well seasoned wood and are graduated accurately with a machine of great precision. T-squares are carefully made from wood and other materials that have been seasoned for months. The painstaking process of making a good T-square really requires months and months.

Drawing instruments and equipment will give the best service only when kept in good condition and not abused. An expert draftsman, just as a real craftsman of any kind, takes the best care of his instruments and tools. He takes pride in keeping the tools of his craft in the best condition.

Drawing instruments should be kept clean at all times. They will give long, accurate service if used and handled with care. These precision instruments are finely constructed and should be used only for the purpose for which they were intended.

Drafting Machine

The drafting machine is used in industrial and commercial drafting rooms because all the instruments such as a T-square, triangle, protractor, and scale are combined in one device, Fig. 59B.

Time is saved with all instruments combined in one machine fastened to the drawing board. At the same time, it assures accurate work on the part of the draftsman when he has been trained to use the machine properly.

The drafting machine is not usually found in the personal kit of the student of mechanical drawing. However, in engineering classes in college, in technical institutes, and in teacher education, considerable use is made of the drafting machine, Fig. 59C. It is fastened to the drawing board and is not easily removed for homework. There is a new portable model available, but it is more costly than the set of separate instruments.

The drafting machine does not take the place of compasses and ruling pens. Therefore, with knowledge and ability to use hand instruments properly in making drawings, your learning to use the drafting machine will come easily. If you had not the knowledge of using drafting instruments, you would be hindered in your progress in learning to use the drafting machine.

Fig. 59C. Drafting Machines in Use (Courtesy, Eastern Kentucky University)

Before plant facilities are changed, thorough planning and model layouts are analyzed for the purposes of: (1) insuring the most effective and efficient use of floor space, (2) minimizing the required manpower in making adjustments in the location of equipment, and (3) to communicate the planners' ideas to the people that will do the moving. (Courtesy International Harvester Co.)

There are two measuring scales used in making drawings. They are the architect's scale and the engineer's scale. The architect's scale is divided into units or fractions such as found on a standard ruler. It is used in making working drawings for the mechanic and the builder. The engineer's scale is divided into decimal units; that is, 10, 20, 30, 40, 50, 60, 80, and 100 parts to an inch. It is used in map drawing.

Scales are sold in the triangular shape as in Fig. 60, or in a thin rectangular shape with beveled edges as in Fig. 61. They are usually made of boxwood. The triangular scale is most popular because of its low cost. It is easy to handle, but it turns over and out of position easily. A paper clip or a special guard, as shown

in Fig. 62, will keep the scale in working position. To protect the first and last graduations of the scale, extra wood is provided at the ends.

Architect's Scale

1. Examine your scale and study the various graduations. Also see Fig. 60.

2. On one edge you will find that the graduations are like those of a common rule. On the adjoining edge, the graduations are marked 1½ at one end and 3 at the opposite end. Observe that the first large space at each end is divided into units like those of the common rule. For example, at one end the first three-inch division is marked to represent a standard rule, but the graduations are much smaller. The three-inch division represents one foot and one of its twelve quarter-inch graduations represents one inch.

3. Continue to turn the scale and observe that the other edges are marked into divisions of 1″ and ½″, ¾″ and ⅜″, ¼″ and ⅛″, ³⁄₁₆″ and

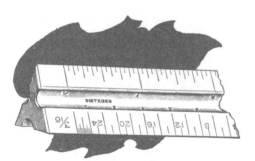

Fig. 60. Triangular Scale

Fig. 62. A Special Clip Keeps the Scale in Position

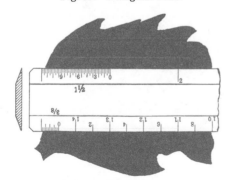

Fig. 61. Rectangular Scale

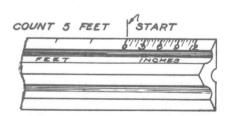

Fig. 63. Using the Scale for Feet Only

³⁄₃₂″. At each end of the scale, the first division is marked off to represent the graduations of a common rule.

4. The special divisions on each edge of the scale are used in making drawings smaller than full size and in proportion. If you wish to make a drawing quarter size or three inches to the foot, you would choose the division marked 3 and imagine that each ¼″ is one inch and proceed to draw.

5. Examine the scale and observe that at each end where the first large unit is marked into graduations representing a common rule, the inner point is marked 0 and the small graduations are numbered higher toward the opposite end. See Fig. 66. These small graduations at the end represent inches. The large graduations, from the 0 mark toward the center of the scale, represent feet.

6. You may be making a drawing at any reduced scale, but if you wish to lay off a dimension in feet only, such as 5 feet, start at the 0 mark and count off five numbered graduations toward the center. Fig. 63.

7. If you wish to lay off a dimension in feet and inches, such as 5′-6″, select the 6 inch graduation toward the end of the scale from the 0 mark and set this graduation at the point from which you wish to measure. Then starting at the 0 mark toward the center on the large graduations, count off 5 feet and place a mark on the paper. See Fig. 64.

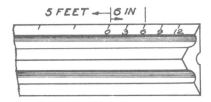

Fig. 64.   Using the Scale for Feet and Inches

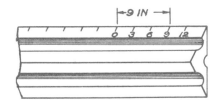

Fig. 65A.   Using the Scale for Inches Only

Avoid moving the scale when making measurements.

8. If you wish to lay off a dimension in inches only, such as 9 inches, start at the 0 mark, and toward the end of the scale lay off nine of the small graduations representing inches. Fig. 65A.

Engineer's Scale

1. The engineer's scale is marked to represent feet and inches, but the graduations are in decimals rather than in fractions. This scale differs from the architect's scale in that the smaller divisions of an inch, such as appear at each end of the architect's scale, appear along its full length. See Fig. 65B.

Laying Off Dimensions

1. Place the scale in position so the light falls on the edge with which you wish to measure, and at the same time be sure the scale is exactly on the line to be measured.

2. Make short light dashes when marking.

3. If you wish to measure several distances on one line, lay them off from one point without moving the scale.

Problems

1. Choose that part of the scale where one inch is equal to one foot. Lay off on a sheet of paper and have approved by your teacher the following measurements: 5′-0″, 0′-9″, 3′-3″, 4′-6″, 2′-7″, 7′-8″.

2. Repeat the measurements by laying them off from the other end of the scale where the half-inch unit represents a foot.

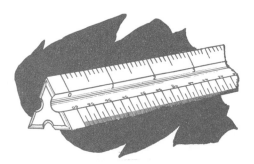

Fig. 65B.   Triangular Engineer's Scale Has Six Edges with Small Graduations

Locating Lines with a Pencil

Little things properly done usually combine to make a larger thing that has the appearance of the work of an expert. The little things, therefore, must have careful attention. For example, marks through which pencil lines are to be drawn can be so carelessly made as to make the drawing ugly and it will not be exact. The expert draftsman makes the pencil layout mark neatly in the form of a short neat dash.

1. Be sure your pencil is sharp.
2. Fasten the paper to the board in position for drawing.
3. Place the scale on the paper in position to lay out the desired line, Fig. 66.
4. Carefully place the pencil next to the scale at the desired measurement and make a short light dash, Fig. 66. The short dash will form a part of the line to be drawn and thus be hidden.
5. To draw the line, place the point of the pencil on the mark, bring the T-square or triangle up to the pencil and proceed with the line.

Questions

1. In drawing a line through a point, it is accurately done and with little strain on the eyes when the pencil is placed on the mark first and the T-square or triangle then brought to it. (True or False)

2. In drawing a line through a point, accuracy can best be obtained with little effort by carefully placing the edge of the T-square or triangle on the point and then drawing the pencil line. (True or False)

3. A large dot is easily seen and therefore is more certain to lead to accurately placed lines. (True or False)

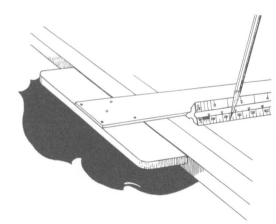

Fig. 66. Make a Short, Light Dash When Laying Out Lines

Drawing Horizontal and Vertical Lines

When making working drawings, the lines are made with instruments. When making working sketches, the lines are made free hand. The important difference is in the manner of making the lines. Accuracy in placing the lines is very important in mechanical drawing. There are several suggestions to follow in attaining accuracy.

1. Wipe the instruments free of dust before starting to work.

2. When drawing, take a position so the light comes from the left. This prevents shadows caused by the T-square, triangles, and scale on your work. The lines will then be in the light.

3. Place the pencil on the dash through which the line is to be drawn and then bring the straightedge up to it.

4. When drawing lines with a pencil and guiding edge, hold the pencil so it is tipped in the direction that the hand moves and slightly outward as shown in Fig. 67. The point of the pencil must be against the blade as it touches the paper. Keep the pencil in the same position throughout to make sure that the line will be perfectly straight.

5. Apply uniform pressure and roll the pencil slightly between the thumb and fingers as the line is drawn.

6. Do not track the pencil back and forth.

Drawing Horizontal Lines

1. Make horizontal lines, Fig. 68, with the upper edge of the T-square as a guide.

2. Be sure that the head of the T-square is snug against the left edge of the drawing board.

   Always place the head of the T-square against the same edge of the drawing board while making a given drawing. The edges of the board are not likely to be square with each other. Therefore, while drawing, if you change the position of the head of the T-square from one edge to another, the lines will not be true with each other.

3. Place the pencil on the dash through which the line is to be drawn, slide the T-square up to it, and draw the line from left to right, sliding the fingers along the blade of the T-square as you draw, Fig. 67.

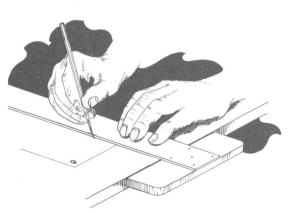

Fig. 67. Tip the Pencil Outward and in the Direction the Hand Moves, Sliding the Little Finger Along the T-Square

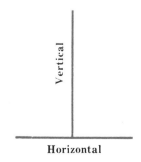

Vertical

Horizontal

Fig. 68. Horizontal and Vertical Lines

Drawing Vertical Lines

1. Vertical lines, Fig. 68, are made with a triangle as a guide.
2. To draw vertical lines, hold the triangle in position against the T-square as shown in Fig. 69.

   Observe that in this position you will be working with your hand over the triangle, thus protecting your work, and at the same time there will be no shadows on the lines as you draw them.

   Form the habit of keeping the triangle snug against the T-square and the head of the T-square snug against the left edge of the board.

3. Place the pencil on the dash, bring the triangle up to it and then draw the line, letting the fingers slide along the triangle as shown in Fig. 69.
4. Draw the line from a point near the T-square toward the top of the triangle as shown by the arrow in Fig. 69.

Fig. 69. Drawing a Vertical Line

Questions

1. In making a straight line, the straightedge should be brought up to the desired point and then the pencil should be placed against the straightedge. (True or False)

2. The pencil may be tracked back and forth when ruling lines. (True or False)

3. When drawing, the head of the T-square is always held against the (A) edge of the board.

4. Horizontal lines are drawn with the (A) edge of the T-square only.

Laying Out
a Drawing Sheet

Drawings are made in standard sizes to make it easier to handle them and to file them. It would be very difficult to keep drawing of many shapes and sizes. This is an important consideration in schools as well as in industry.

The most common basic sizes are 8½" x 11" or 9" x 12". Larger drawings are made in proportion, as 12" x 18" and 18" x 24". These sizes may be cut from large sheets or rolls of drawing paper without wasting the paper. Small size drawings may be easily folded and mailed with a letter. Economy is practiced in industry and large sheets of paper are not used when small ones will do.

Border lines are drawn on all plates to improve appearance and to limit the area to be used for the drawing. A special record or title strip is placed at the bottom of every drawing in industry as well as in school.

This record strip, as used in school, gives the names of the school, the object drawn, and the student; it gives the scale, drawing number, and date when the drawing was finished. The initials of the person who traced, checked, or approved it, and the date of completion of the tracing are frequently given.

All this information and more is necessary in industry. You are, as nearly as is possible, going

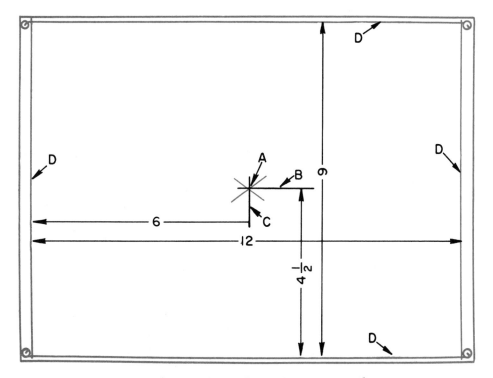

Fig. 70. First Step in Laying Out a Drawing Sheet

to follow the practice of industry in making your drawings. These directions are for laying out a 9″ x 12″ sheet.

Locating the Center of the Sheet

1. With a straightedge, locate the center of the sheet by drawing diagonal lines from the corners of the sheet. See *A*, Fig. 70.
2. Fasten the paper to the board. See Unit 15.

Drawing the Cutting Lines

1. Draw, lightly, a horizontal line and a vertical line through the center, as at *B* and *C*, Fig. 70. These will serve as guides in measuring accurately.

Drawing the Border Lines

1. On line *B* in Fig. 70, lay off horizontally from the center of the sheet, 5½″ in each direction.
2. On line *C* in Fig. 70, lay off vertically from the center of the sheet 4″ in each direction.

3. Draw four lines through the marks located in steps 1 and 2 until they meet in the corners. These will be lines *E* in Fig. 71 and will be the border lines of the finished drawing.

Drawing the Record Strip

1. Lay off vertically one half inch from the lower border line.
2. Draw a horizontal line, *F*, connecting the two border lines at the ends of the drawing sheet.
3. Lay off the vertical divisions for the record strip as shown in Fig. 71.

   If you are using 8½″ x 11″ paper, make the sections of the record strip ¼″ shorter than is shown in Fig. 72, which is dimensioned for 9″ x 12″ paper.
4. Do not lay off the guide lines for lettering until the drawing has been completed. Leave the record strip as in Fig. 71. It will be completed after the drawing is made.
5. Check all measurements to see that you have made no mistakes in laying out the sheet.

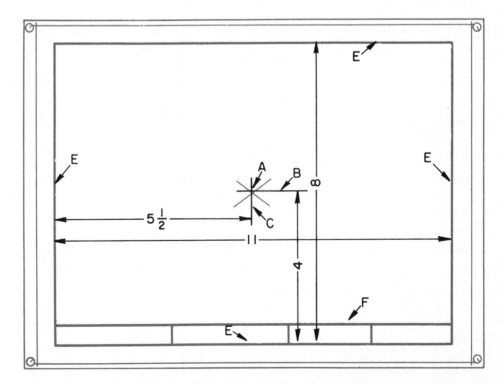

Fig. 71. Second Step in Laying Out a Drawing Sheet

Completing the Record Strip

In industry, the *record strip* on drawings includes production and reference information. The record strip in Fig. 72B is satisfactory for instructional records. Industrial drafting rooms usually have standard forms for record strips. Tracing cloth or paper may include a printed form for the record strip which is filled in by the person checking or making the drawing, Fig. 72A.

A typical form would include:

(1) name of the company,

(2) name of the part or machine,

(3) number of the drawing,

(4) scale,

(5) number of parts to be manufactured,

(6) material,

(7) identifying numbers if there is a set of drawings that includes details and assembly,

(8) initials and date of the draftsman, checker, tracer, and the approving authority, and

(9) other data such as special metal treatment, limits in fitting, finish, or revisions.

The record strip on industrial drawings will require more information than the record strip suggested in this book. You will be provided with the necessary form when you have a need for it but the method suggested in this book has provided you with some knowledge of the purposes and information required on a record strip.

1. The record strip is to be completed only after you have finished the drawing and have checked it.

2. Examine Fig. 72B and observe that the guide lines in sections 1, 3, and 4 are spaced alike. They start with a $\frac{1}{16}''$ space and are $\frac{1}{8}''$ apart, leaving another $\frac{1}{16}''$ space. There are three $\frac{1}{8}''$ spaces, which give space for two lines of lettering.

3. Observe that the guide lines in section 2 are different from those in the other sections. This section is laid out in this way when

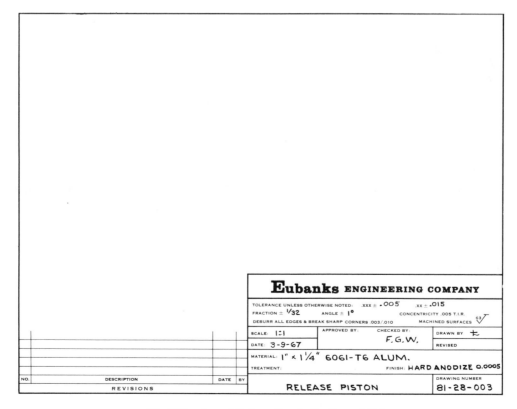

Fig. 72A. Record Information in the Record Strip

only one space ¾₁₆″ high is needed. When the scale of the drawing is to be given with the title, use the layout form shown in A, Fig. 72B.

4. In only one space lay out the guide lines for sections 1, 3, and 4. With one setting of the T-square, draw each line across the sheet in all three sections that are alike. Examine Fig. 72B.

5. Draw the lines for section 2 according to the space needed for the number of words in the title. Learn to judge quickly the space required.

6. After you have had instruction and practice in lettering as outlined in Unit 10, fill in the necessary information in the spaces as indicated in Fig. 72B. Your instructor will tell you what to place in section 1 of the record strip on your drawings.

Questions

1. Why locate the center of the sheet as the first step in laying out the drawing to be made?
2. Why not draw guide lines for the lettering and do the lettering in the record strip until the drawing itself has been completely finished?
3. Time is saved by drawing as many lines as is possible with one setting of the T-square or triangle. (True or False)
4. Why not trim the cutting edge before the object lines have been strengthened and all other lines have been put into approved form?

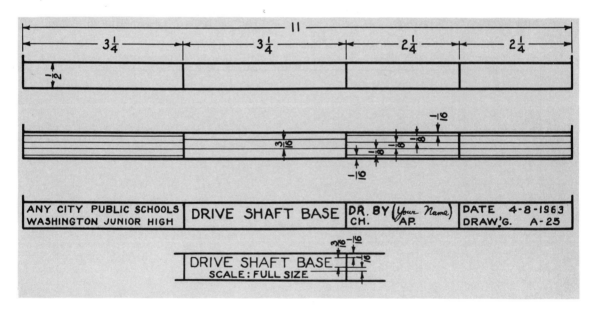

Fig. 72B. Dimensions for Laying Out the Record Strip

Blocking in a Drawing
with Instruments

One who makes working drawings, whether he is a draftsman, engineer, architect, or a student, must not only work rapidly, but he must use the best methods and the most economical order of procedure. Laying out a drawing on paper may take considerable time unless attention is given to an orderly way of doing it. It is not by haste that speed is attained; it is by orderly and thoughtful procedure, and, of course, practice.

Make a sketch of your drawing first. Place each view in its proper location and each dimension line in the place where it is to be located in the drawing. The making of the mechanical drawing will be the copying of the sketch with the drawing instruments, with all measurements accurate.

Place the views near the center of the sheet, if views for one object are to be drawn. Although you should not go to laborious measuring to locate the drawing near the center of the sheet, the following instruction will be helpful in locating views.

When a Top and Front View are Required

1. Add the height of the front view, the distance between views, ordinarily an inch, and the depth (vertical distance across) of the top view. The total distance is represented by A in Fig. 73.

2. To locate the bottom of the front view, lay off B, Fig. 73, one-half of distance A, less ¼″, (the record strip being ½″ high[1]) below the center of the sheet. If it is necessary to place some dimensions below the front view, enough space for them must be allowed or the drawing will not appear centered.

3. To locate the left side of the drawing, lay off C, one-half the length of the front view, including dimensions, to the left of the center of the sheet.

4. Starting with the location of the bottom of the front view, lay off vertically the height of the front view, the distance between views, and the depth of the top view. From the location of the left side of the front view, lay off the horizontal length of the drawing.

When a Front and Side View are Required

1. Add the width of the front view (horizontal

---

[1] The space within the border lines of a 9″ x 12″ drawing sheet is 8″ x 11″. When a record strip ½″ high is used, the space left for drawing is 7½ x 11″. The upper border is made 4″ above the center of the sheet. The center of the drawing space is 3¾″ below the upper border. It is clear then that the center of the sheet is ¼″ below the center of the drawing space. To bring the drawing in the center of the space, then, the bottom of the drawing will be ¼″ less than half its height below the center of the sheet. This will also hold true if the sheet is 8½″ x 11″.

If a record strip ¾″ high is used, it will be necessary to subtract ⅜″ instead of ¼″ from one-half the whole height of the drawing to determine the center of the sheet for drawing.

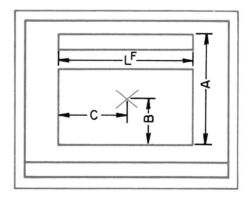

Fig. 73. Top View Drawing Blocked In

distance across), the distance between views, and the depth in the side view (distance across) to find *D*, the total width of the drawing.

2. To locate the left end of the front view, lay off *E*, one-half the total distance across the two views, to the left of the center of the sheet.

3. To locate the bottom of the front view, lay off *F*, one-half the vertical height of the front view, less ¼″, below the center of the sheet. If it is necessary to place some dimensions below the front view, enough space for them must be allowed.

4. Starting with the location of the left end of the front view, lay off the horizontal distance across the front view, the distance between the views, and the depth in the side view.

5. From the location of the bottom of the front view, lay off the height of the front view of the drawing.

When a Three-View Drawing is Required

1. Locate the bottom of the front view, Fig. 75, in the same way as in making the two-view drawing showing the front and top, Fig. 73. Locate the left side of the front view in the same way as in making a two-view drawing showing the front and side, Fig. 74.

2. Lay off the width of the front view, the distance between views and the depth in the side view. See instructions given in preceding Step 4.

After Locating the Views

1. With fine, light lines and through the points thus located, draw the main outlines of each view first. Draw the details of the drawing last.

2. Draw horizontal lines at the top of the drawing first, working toward the bottom until all are drawn. Draw vertical lines at the left side of the drawing first, working toward the right.

3. Make as many lines as possible with the T-square and triangle while you are working with each of them. Get into the habit of doing all you can with one instrument before you lay it down. This practice will save time and give cleaner drawings.

4. Be sure that you make the lines meet at all corners. If the lines overlap at the corners, you can erase them later.

5. Check the views and their sizes for accuracy.

Questions

1. Placing the drawing near the center of the sheet is necessary for well balanced appearance. It has no relation to the meaning of the drawing as far as the views are concerned. (True or False)

2. The process of laying out the views is called (A).

3. Draw (A) lines at the top of the drawing first working toward the bottom of the sheet.

4. Draw (B) lines at the left side of the sheet first, working toward the right side of the drawing.

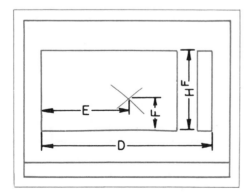

Fig. 74. Two-View Drawing Blocked In

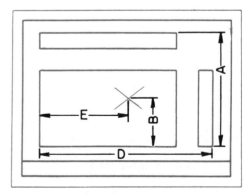

Fig. 75. Three-View Drawing Blocked In

Making a Simple Working Drawing

A draftsman may make drawings that require one, two or three views. An example of a one-view drawing would be the drawing of a plat for a lot or a city block, or a map. A drawing of an object cut from thin material, such as a templet or a gasket would require only one view, Figs. 76, 77, and 78. A round shaft would require but one view if a section is shown.

An object should be drawn with *two views* if the complete shape and size can thus be shown, Fig. 79. The workman must have a clear idea of shape and the thickness, width, and length of the object and its parts. If two views will not give all the necessary information, a third view may be necessary, Fig. 80A.

The best way to determine whether there is enough information is to imagine that you are the workman that must use the drawing, Fig. 80B. If you can find all the information that you need, then you have drawn enough views and given enough dimensions. A draftsman should know how to make the things that he draws.

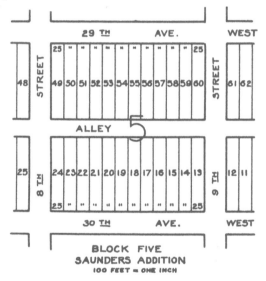

Fig. 76

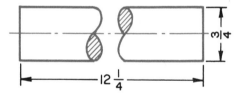

Fig. 78. Shafting

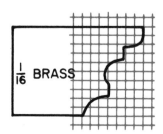

Fig. 77. Template for a Moulding, Full Size

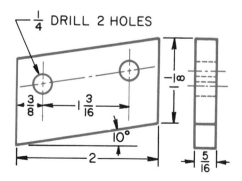

Fig. 79. Knife for Bench Shears, Full Size

1. Make a working sketch showing the necessary views, center lines, and dimensions and have it approved by the instructor.
2. Lay out the sheet.
3. Determine the scale.
4. Block in the general views, working from the sketch.
5. Draw center lines for symmetrical parts and circles.
6. Draw in the circles and arcs.
7. Place the dimension lines in the proper places you planned for them in the working sketch.
8. Make the arrowheads and dimension figures.
9. Check the drawing and see that it is complete.
10. Go over all object lines with a sharp *4H* pencil, making the lines black so they stand out clearly.
11. Fill in the record strip with the proper information.
12. Go over the border lines and enclosing lines of the record strip with a sharp *4H* pencil, making them black.
13. Hand in the drawing for final approval by the instructor.

Questions

1. A drawing of a city lot requires (A) view(s) and it is called a (B).
2. A working sketch need be made only when drawings of extreme importance are desired. (True or False)

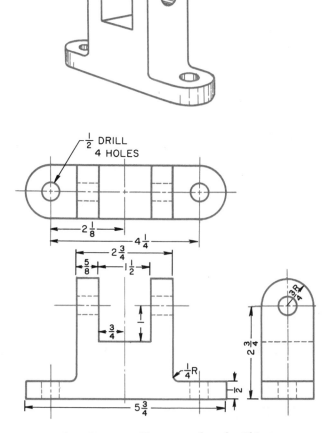

Fig. 80A. Three Views are Necessary when the Object
has Several Details

3. Inspecting a working drawing to see that all necessary information has been given is called (A).

4. A drawing of a baseball bat would require (A) view(s), one being a sectional view.

5. A drawing of a bicycle sprocket wheel would require (A) view(s).

6. Why should a shim or gasket or templet require but one view?

7. Here are pictures of seven objects. If a working drawing was to be made of each object, either one, two, or three views would be necessary. Study each object and determine the necessary views. You can do this best by making a sketch of each view on scrap paper. A letter is placed under each picture. Place the letter of the object under the sketch of the views that belong to it.

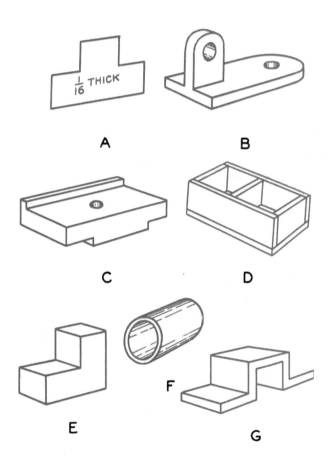

Fig. 80B. The Difficulty of the Object Determines the Number of Views Required

PROBLEMS

Required: Simple two-view working drawings of objects with straight visible outlines. Make a free-hand sketch of each drawing and have it checked before making the mechanical drawing.

Problem 1: Sand Block

Over-all dimensions, ¾″ x 2″ x 4″.

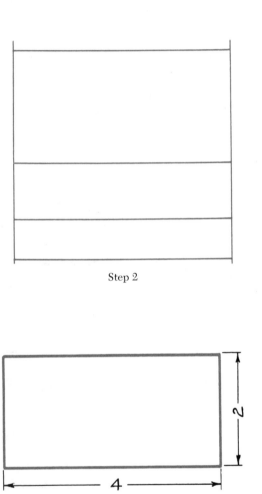

Step 2

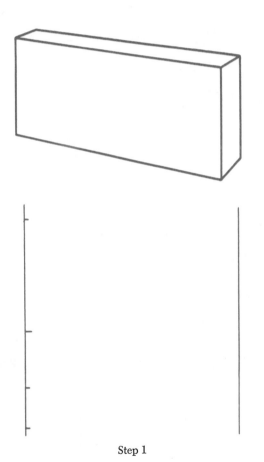

Step 1

Step 3

Problem 2: Vise Liner Block

Over-all dimensions, ½″ x 4″ x 7″.

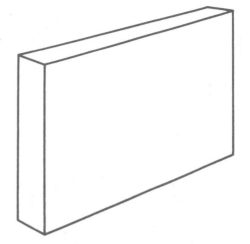

Problem 2 — Vise Liner Block

Problem 3: Seat

Over-all dimensions, 2″ x 3″ x 5″.
Seat, 2″ x 2″ x 1″.

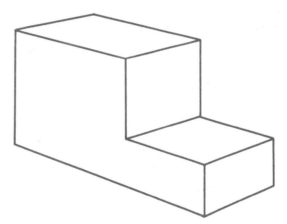

Problem 3 — Seat

Problem 4: Weight

Base, 1″ x 2″ x 6″.
Pad, ⅜″ x 1¼″ x 4¼″.

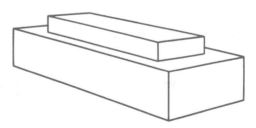

Problem 4 — Weight

Checking a Drawing

There are many persons who have not learned how important it is to check their work to see if there are mistakes. They are not now employed as successfully as they could be if they would develop the habit of checking their work. To make mistakes is human, but to discover and correct them requires training and an attitude of willingness to do things right. Since working drawings tell the workman what to do, there must be no mistakes in them.

In order to prevent mistakes, check the drawing:

1. For location on the sheet and general appearance.
   a. Have you placed the drawing near the center of the sheet?
   b. Is the drawing neat and clean?

2. For relative position, choice and correctness of views.
   a. Are the views in proper relation to each other?
   b. Have the views been carefully projected?
   c. Are there center lines for all circles and symmetrical objects?

3. For position and correctness of dimensions and notes.
   a. Are all necessary dimensions given? Are thickness, width, and length given for the object and any of its parts that require dimensions?
   b. Are the dimensions found easily; that is, are related dimensions together so the worker will not be required to hunt for them?
   c. Have you repeated any dimensions?
   d. Have you made all calculations and have you checked them to see that over-all and detail dimensions go together?
   e. Do all dimension figures and notes read easily from the lower right of the drawing?

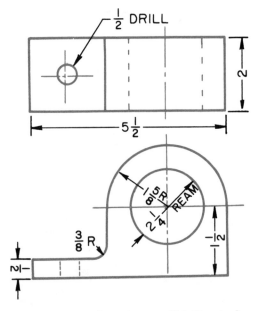

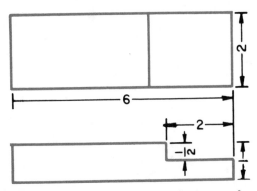

Fig. 81. How Many Errors in This Drawing?

Fig. 82. Are There Errors in This Drawing?

4. For well formed, uniform lettering, figures, and arrowheads.

   a. Have you lettered the record strip with all necessary information?

   b. Have you spelled all words on the drawing correctly and lettered them well?

   c. Are all arrowheads properly made and in their proper places?

5. For form and contrast of lines, tangents, and corners.

   a. Have all lines been made so they conform to the adopted standard for lines?

   b. Where one line is intended, are there any double ones?

   c. Do all corner lines meet exactly?

   d. When arcs, circles, and straight lines meet, do they form perfect connections?

Questions

1. In Figs. 81 and 82 there are mistakes that may be found by checking carefully steps 2, 3, 4, and 5. Examine the drawings and you will find 7 corrections to be made in the first drawing and 13 corrections to be made in the second drawing.

Drawing Views with Hidden Outlines

In making working drawings it is often necessary to show construction that is hidden from view. In order to prevent confusion with the visible parts, hidden edges are represented by the hidden outlines shown and described in the learning unit on conventional lines.

There are certain ways to draw these lines in order to make the drawing as clear as possible.

1. In Figures 83, 84, and 85 are views with hidden outlines properly shown.

2. Always start a hidden-object line with a dash. Observe this in Figs. 83 and 84 at points A.

3. When two hidden surfaces are supposed to come together and are represented by hidden outlines, see that they touch exactly as at B in Fig. 84. Since a hidden outline represents a surface, if the lines at B did not touch it would mean that the surfaces did not come together.

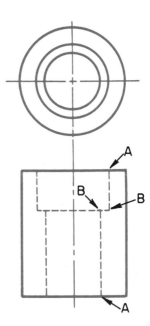

Fig. 84. Drawing with Hidden Outline

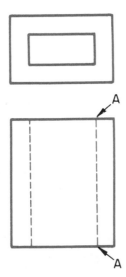

Fig. 83. Drawing with Hidden Outline

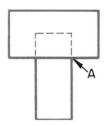

Fig. 85. Drawing with Hidden Outline

4. When a hidden outline is a continuation of a visible outline as A, Fig. 85, leave a space between the visible object line and the hidden outline.

5. When a hidden outline becomes visible, as in a sectional view, then the line must be made a visible outline.

6. Study Figs. 86 and 87 and observe how the view with a hidden outline is made. You should study this, or even draw it, before attempting the problems your teacher will assign.

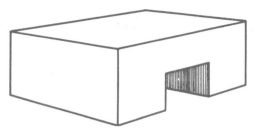

Fig. 86. Channel Block

Questions

1. A hidden outline represents a (A).

2. A hidden outline is made of (A) dashes and (B) spaces alternating. The line is only a little (C) than visible outlines.

3. On a separate sheet of paper make sketches of the accompanying drawings, correcting the incorrect lines and indicate them, Fig. 88.

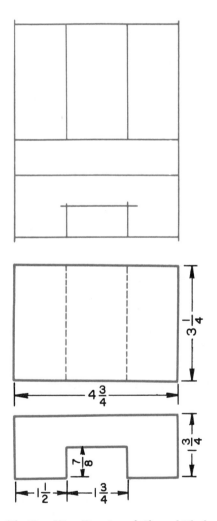

Fig. 87. Two-View Drawing of Channel Block

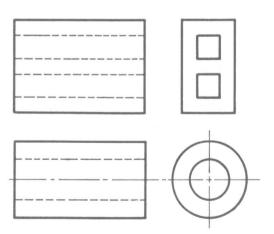

Fig. 88. Are These Drawings Properly Made?

PROBLEMS

Required: Working drawings of objects with straight visible and hidden outlines.

Problem 1: Mortised Block

Data:
Outside dimensions, 1¼″ x 2″ x 5″.
Mortise in the center of the piece, ⅜″ x 2″ x 2″.

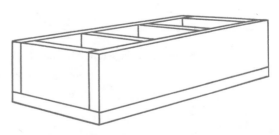

Problem 1 — Mortised Block

Problem 2: Hot Dish Stand

Data:
Over-all dimensions, 1¼″ x 6″ x 6″.
Size of feet, ¼″ x 1¼″ x 1¼″.

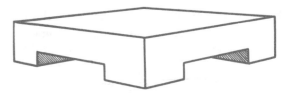

Problem 2 — Hot Dish Stand

Problem 3: U-Block

Data:
Outside dimensions, 2″ x 3″ x 5″.
Groove in the center of the upper face, ⅜″ x 3″.
Groove in the center of the bottom, ⅜″ x 1″ x 5″.

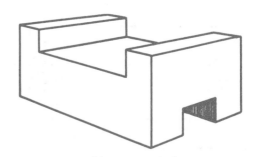

Problem 3 — U-Block

Problem 4: Nail Box

Data:
Over-all dimensions, 1¾″ x 3½″ x 8″.
Thickness of bottom, ½″.
Thickness of sides and ends, ⅜″.
Thickness of partitions, ¼″.
Material, white pine or basswood.
Space partitions for 2¼″ opening.

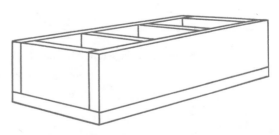

Problem 4 — Nail Box

Problem 5: Jig

Data:
A = 2″
B = 2¾″
C = 1½″
D = ¾″
E = ½″
F = ¼″
G = 1¼″

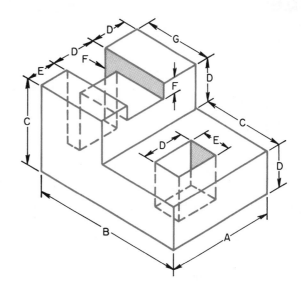

Problem 5 — Jig

Problem 6. Fixture

Data:
A = 2″   E = ¾″
B = 3″   F = ½″
C = 1½″   G = ⅜″
D = 1″   H = ⅝″
              I = ¼″

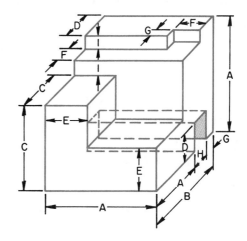

Problem 6 — Fixture

Sketching Angles

In making sketches of all kinds of objects, you will often find that lines at 30°, 45°, and 60° must be sketched. An accurate picture of the comparative size of angles will be of great help.

Forty-Five Degree Angle

1. A right angle, the sides of which are square with each other, is measured as 90°, Fig. 89. You can readily see that an angle half as large would have the sides spread apart only half as far and be a 45° angle, Fig. 90.

Fig. 89. Ninety Degree Angle

Fig. 90. Forty-Five Degree Angle

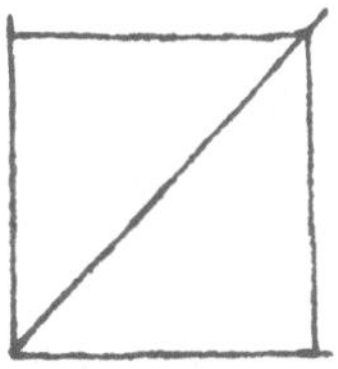

Fig. 91. Square Used to Determine Forty-Five Degree Angle

2. Sketch very lightly a half-inch square, one side of which will form the side of a 45° angle, Fig. 91.

3. Sketch the diagonal of the square. This will give the direction of the 45° line, Fig. 91.

4. Darken the sides of the angle. If only a line at 45° is desired, darken only the required line.

5. After a little experience you will need to sketch only two sides of the square or a right angle. Then divide the right angle to obtain the 45° angle, Fig. 92.

6. If you have carefully observed the spread of the sides of a 45° angle you should have a good picture of the angle in your "mind's eye." You should be able to sketch a line at 45° without first sketching either a square or a right angle, Fig. 93.

7. Lines at 45° to the horizontal are called 45° lines.

Fig. 92. Forty-Five Degree Angle Sketched with only Two Sides of the Square as Guides

Fig. 93. Forty-Five Degree Line

Thirty and Sixty Degree Angles

1. An examination of Fig. 94 will help you to observe that a 30° angle is two-thirds as large as a 45° angle, having its sides spread apart 30°.

2. Further, a 60° angle has its sides spread twice as far as a 30° angle, Fig. 95.

3. Observe these angles very closely.

4. Sketch one side of the angle.

5. Estimate the required spread of the sides and sketch the other side of the angle.

6. Lines at 30° to the horizontal are called 30° lines; at 60° to horizontal they are called 60° lines, Fig. 96.

Questions

1. The 45° angle is (A) times as large as a 30° angle.

2. A 45° angle is (A) of a 60° angle.

3. A 60° angle is (A) times as large as a 45° angle.

4. A 75° angle is what part of a 60° angle larger?

5. Sketch two lines at 45°; at 60°; at 30°.

Fig. 94.   Thirty Degree Angle

Fig. 95.   Sixty Degree Angle

Fig. 96.   Sixty, Forty-Five, and Thirty Degree Lines

Unit

25

Drawing Inclined Lines

Inclined lines are also called *oblique lines.* Any line that is neither horizontal nor vertical is inclined, or oblique.

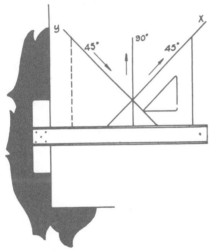

Fig. 97. To Draw Lines at 45°

1. To draw lines at 45° with the horizontal, use the 45° triangle. Place it against the T-square as shown in Fig. 97, and proceed as in drawing vertical lines. If the lines are to be inclined as at X, Fig. 97, draw the lines toward the top of the triangle as shown by the arrow. If the lines are to be inclined as at Y, Fig. 1, draw the lines toward the T-square, as shown by the arrow.

2. To draw lines at 30° or 60° with the horizontal, place the 30°-60° triangle in the necessary position, as shown in Figs. 98 and 99. Proceed as in step 1.

3. To draw lines at 15° or 75° with the horizontal, place the 45° and 30°-60° triangles as shown in Fig. 100.

4. Study Figs. 97, 98, 99, 100, and 101 and you will see how circles or parts of circles can be divided with the triangles into units of 15°, 30°, 45°, 60°, and 90°.

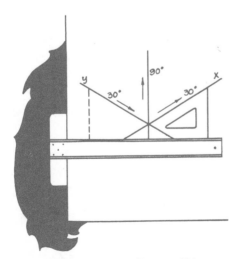

Fig. 98. To Draw Lines at 30°

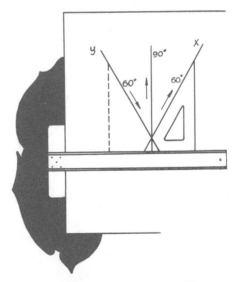

Fig. 99. To Draw Lines at 60°

5. To draw lines at angles that cannot be made with the triangles, use the protractor, as shown in Fig. 102. Place the center *A* on the point through which the inclined line is to be drawn, slide the T-square into place, and check to see that the center is still in position. Place a short dash, *B*, at the desired angle as indicated on the protractor.

6. Remove the protractor, and with a straight-edge, draw the line through *A* and *B*.

Questions

1. The triangle can be used without the aid of the T-square for drawing vertical lines. (True or False)

2. To draw a line 75° with the horizontal, place the (A) triangle against the T-square and place the (B) triangle against the first triangle.

3. Why draw the inclined lines in the direction shown in Fig. 97?

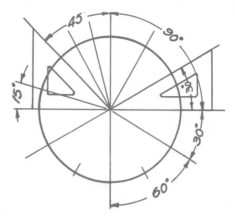

Fig. 101. Use the Triangle to Divide a Circle into Units of 15°, 30°, 45°, 60° and 75°

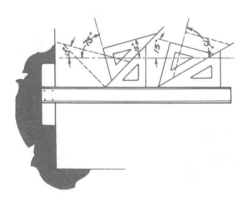

Fig. 100. To Draw Lines at 15° and 75°

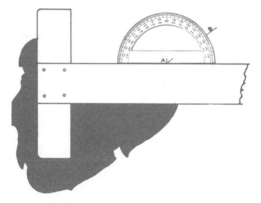

Fig. 102. Use the Protractor for Inclined Lines that Cannot be Drawn with the Triangle

Unit 26

Drawing Lines Parallel

It may be necessary to draw sloping parallel lines at some angle other than the standard angles, 15°, 30°, 45°, 60°, or 75°. To do so it will be impossible to use the T-square and triangles as in drawing the standard angles.

1. If you wish to draw several lines parallel with each other, draw the first line in the desired position.

2. Hold the triangle to the first line and move the blade of the T-square, or a triangle, up to it, as shown in Fig. 103.

3. Hold the T-square firmly in position with the thumb and little finger of the left hand and slide the triangle, as shown in Fig. 104. Draw with the right hand as in drawing vertical lines with the triangle.

4. Continue to draw the required number of parallel lines, being careful to hold the T-square firmly in position as you slide the triangle into place for each line.

Questions

1. Lines can be drawn parallel to a line that has already been drawn by sliding the triangle up to it and continuing as in drawing new parallel lines. (True or False)

2. If you have only three or four parallel lines to draw, it would be easier to use another triangle for a guide instead of the T-square. (True or False)

Fig. 103. Hold the Triangle to the First Line and Bring the T-Square Blade up to It

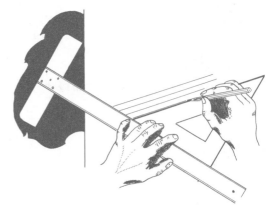

Fig. 104. To Draw Parallel Lines

Transferring Distances and Spacing with Dividers

Dividers are similar in appearance to compasses, Fig. 105. The legs, however, are unlike those of the compasses in that they are fixed and sharply pointed. Just as with the compasses, dividers are sold in the plain as well as in the bow-type. The latter are ordinarily called bow dividers. These are usually found in every set of drawing instruments.

Dividers are used for transferring distances and for spacing by trial. The bow dividers are used in working with small measurements.

Adjusting and Holding the Dividers

1. Hold the dividers in one hand. Release the tension on the screw. Then open the dividers by pressing the legs apart with the thumb and first finger. Then hold the second and third fingers between the legs with the thumb and first finger on the outside of the legs, Open and close the dividers as desired by pressing in or out with the fingers, Fig. 106.

2. To adjust bow dividers, hold them in one hand and with the thumb and first finger of the other turn the adjusting nut. Release the screw tension by slight pressure on the legs.

Transferring Distances

1. Set the dividers to the desired distance and transfer it to its new location, pressing the points lightly on the paper, just enough to see the marks.

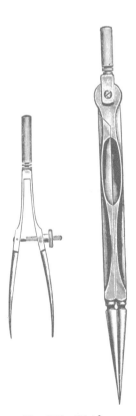

Fig. 105. Dividers

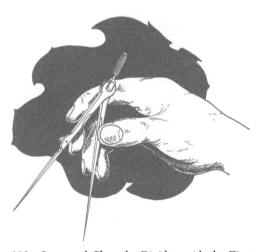

Fig. 106. Open and Close the Dividers with the Fingers

2. Draw, lightly, with a pencil a small ring around each point so you can find it again.

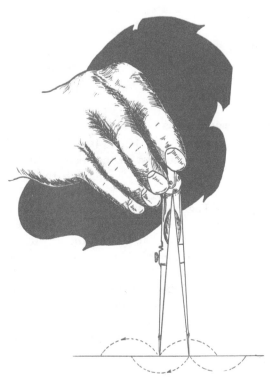

Fig. 107. Swing the Dividers from One Side to the Other

Spacing by Trial

1. Determine the number of equal distances you wish laid off on a given length of line. Suppose you wish to space off three equal distances on a line four inches long.
2. By estimating, set the dividers to one-third the distance.
3. Lay this distance off on the line three times. In moving the dividers from one point to another, swing the legs first from one side of the line then to the other, Fig. 107.
4. If there is a space left over, add one-third of the remaining space to the setting of the dividers and lay off the distances again. Continue to change the dividers until the last space comes out even.
5. If the setting is too long, shorten it one-third the extra space, and try again as in step 4.

Questions

1. Why swing the dividers alternately from one side of the line to the other when spacing? Why not move the dividers by revolving them in one direction?
2. The point made by the dividers should be so (A) that it must be (B) with a (C).

Bisecting a Straight Line

To bisect a line means to divide it into two equal parts. A line may be bisected with a triangle and the T-square, or with the compasses. The first method is the most practical for draftsmen to use because it can be done quickly and accurately.

Bisecting With a Triangle and the T-Square

1. Let line *AB* be the line to be bisected, Fig. 108.

2. With either the 45° or the 30°-60° triangle, draw lines *AC* and *BC* so they intersect, Fig. 109. Draw only enough of each line so as to form the intersection at *C*.

3. With the T-square and a triangle in position for drawing a vertical line, draw line *CD*, Fig. 110. Point *D* locates the center of line *AB*, and distance *AD* will equal distance *DB*.

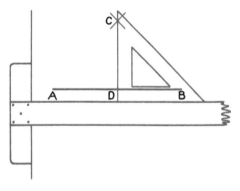

Fig. 110. Second Step in Bisecting Line AB

Fig. 108. Line to be Bisected

Fig. 111. Line to be Bisected

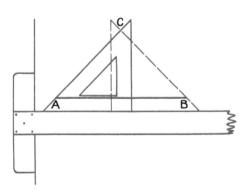

Fig. 109. First Step in Bisecting Line AB

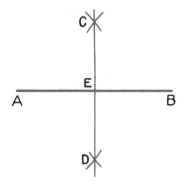

Fig. 112. Line Bisected with Compasses

Bisecting With Compasses

1. Let line *AB* be the line to be bisected, Fig. 111.

2. With the compasses set for a radius greater than half of *AB*, and with *A* and *B* as centers, draw arcs intersecting at *C* and *D*.

3. Draw line *CD*, dividing the line *AB* into equal parts *AE* and *EB*, Fig. 112.

4. Could the method shown in Fig. 112 be used on the athletic field to lay out a square corner?

5. Could a rope and two wooden pegs be used as a compass to strike arcs?

PROBLEMS

Required: Working drawings of objects with inclined lines.

Problem 1: Seat Bracket

Data:
Over-all dimensions, 1″ x 3″ x 5″
Slope, 30° beginning ⅜″ from base

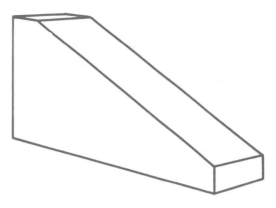

Problem 1 — Seat Bracket

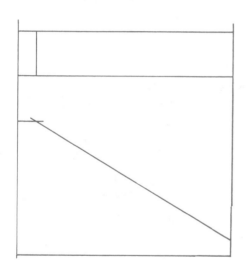

Step 1

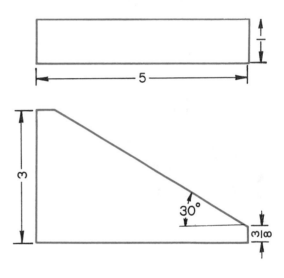

Step 2

Problem 2: Plane Block

Data:
Over-all dimensions, 1¼″ x 3⅞″ x 6″
Ends of the V are ¾″ from ends of piece and at angle of 30°

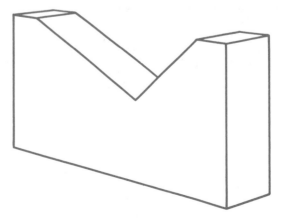

Problem 2 — Plane Block

83

Problem 3: Line Winder

Data:

Over-all dimensions, ½″ x 4″ x 6″
Sides of the V's are at 60° to the ends
Width of V's at the widest part, 3″
Depth of V's, 1¾″

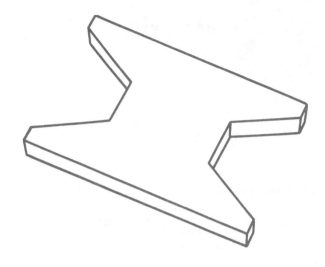

Problem 3 — Line Winder

Problem 4: Gibbed Way

Data:

Over-all dimensions, 1½″ x 4¼″ x 5½″
Width of dovetail at top, 2¼″; depth, ⅝″
Angle of dovetail, 45°
Dovetail centered in the width

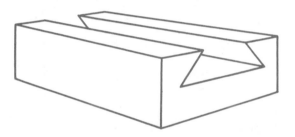

Problem 4 — Gibbed Way

Problem 5: Cross Arm

Data:

Over-all dimensions, 2″ x 3.5″ x 4.5″
Gibbed way, .625″ deep, 1.375″ from end at
  angle of 45°
Slide, .375″ thick, .625″ from side at angle of
  45°

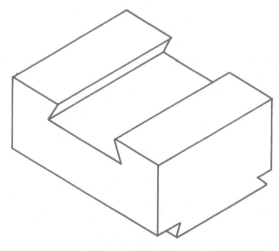

Problem 5 — Cross Arm

Problem 6: Block Pattern

Data:
A = 3″
B = 2¾″
C = 1″
D = ¾″
E = 2″
G = 2½″

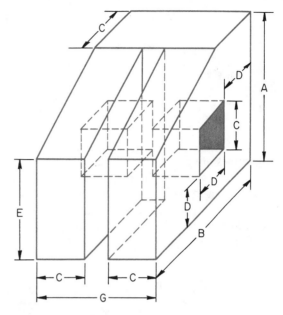

Problem 6 — Block Pattern

The Work and Opportunities of the Mechanical Engineer

Machines are designed and made to do work of all kinds; to make all sorts of usable things to eat, to wear, to shelter our bodies, and to travel from one place to another. Machines are needed to prepare food for the market and the table, to prepare toilet articles, medicines, and beverages.

Knitting machines, weaving machines and shoe machines make wearing apparel. There also are the locomotives, spacecraft engines, automobiles, street cars, and steamships for transportation. Machines also prepare lumber and steel for buildings, make nails, screws, bolts, and fasteners of all

Fig. 113. Gemini 5 Spacecraft Ready for Launching (Courtesy, NASA) Development and production of this huge project required the knowledge and efforts of many engineers, scientists, draftsmen, and skilled technicians.

kinds, pipe, wire, and many, many other articles in everyday use.

Mechanical engineering has to do with the design, construction, and operation of machines. Automobile, aeronautical, hydraulic, marine, air-conditioning, machine tool, farm machinery, and steam engineering are some of the important fields of mechanical engineering. Spacecraft engineering is one of the newest areas of mechanical engineering.

In 1967 there were about 25 different kinds of engineering with approximately 1,000,000 professional engineers employed in the United States.[1] There will be an increasing need for engineers in the years ahead. The want-ads of the Sunday metropolitan newspapers provide good evidence of the current opportunities relating to employment of engineers.

Mechanical engineering is the second largest of the engineering professions. In 1967 there were almost 200,000 mechanical engineers; about three-fourths of these were employed in manufacturing industries. Government agencies, self-employment, and teaching accounted for the remaining one-fourth.[2]

In this unit, attention will be given to the design and construction of machines, which is

[1]Bureau of Labor Statistics, U.S. Department of Labor: Washington, D.C., 1968-69. Bulletin No. 1550, pp. 64ff.
[2]*Ibid.*

the chief work of mechanical engineers. Because of keen competition there is great demand for better and more attractive machines at less cost for material and for work. There is ever a search for ideas for just this purpose. In manufacturing, consideration is given to the need of cutting the costs of production, to the desire to meet the demand for changing styles, and to the requirements for the installation of safety devices. Other elements also are carefully considered. Inventors, designers, draftsmen, and operators of machines submit many ideas, but all cannot be accepted because of poor design or because of the excessive cost of manufacture.

With ever-increasing automatic operation of machines, which is often called *automation*, the work of designers and mechanical engineers is becoming increasingly more important and technical. Automatic control of machines includes drafting as well as the manufacture of articles or parts. Computers are being used in nearly all steps of manufacture as the work of engineers and designers becomes more technical and efficient. The control room for the computer system in an aircraft plant is shown in Fig. 114.

Designing

When a design which seems to have promise has been offered, it is submitted to the head of the experimental department. He in turn sub-

Fig. 114. Computer System in the Computation Center of a Large Manufacturing Company (Courtesy, Douglas Aircraft Corporation)

mits it to experienced designers. They make preliminary sketches of what seems to be the most suitable design, or perhaps alternate schemes for comparison. These preliminary designs are submitted to a committee of engineers, management, and sales people, who decide on the value of the device as a commercial product and whether the company can manufacture and sell it profitably.

If the preliminary designs are approved, the designers commence work on the *assembly layout.* An assembly layout shows all the parts in their relative size and position. The drawings are done in pencil and are handed to the plant engineers for suggestions. After going over the layout to discover any difficulties of production, they return the drawings with their suggestions. The designers then make whatever changes have been suggested and prepare *final designs,* full-size, or to as large a scale as possible.

Dimensioned working drawings, known as *detail drawings,* are made of each part. These are done in pencil in case any changes may have to be made later.

When the experimental machine has been built and tested and any necessary changes made, the drawings are modified in keeping with the changes. If the machine proves satisfactory in the test, the production of the machine or product is recommended by a board of engineers. This ends the long weeks of careful work in the experimental department where men with engineering training and experience and many helpers such as draftsmen and laboratory assistants are required.

The preparation for making the machine also is a long process. Drawings must be prepared for the various production departments, for assembly, and for installation. Tools have to be designed and made.

Engineering Drawings

The general drafting department is given the task of making detail drawings of each part of the machine to be built. The tool designing branch of the drafting department designs and makes detail drawings of the tools needed to make the product. Tools here mean machine tools, jig and fixtures, small tools, and gages. Machine tools really are machines for shaping parts of other machines. Jigs and fixtures are made to hold the work while tool operations are performed and help make all parts alike. When the penciled detail drawings have been completed, they usually are traced in ink, carefully checked and approved; blueprints or other forms of reproduced copies are made and sent to the various shops.

The costs of designing the item and preparing the drawings and specifications often amount to ten or twelve per cent of the entire cost of a large project like a steamship, as well as many other manufactured products.

As already described *final designs* or layouts to large scale are made by draftsmen known as layout men. Machine drawings are usually prepared for purposes of producing, assembling, and installing the machines. For production purposes, an accurate drawing which fully describes the shape, the relationship of one feature to another, and the size is required of each part that is not standard. Bolts, keys, screws, and many similar things have been standardized by manufacturers. Drawings showing a single part in detail are known as detail drawings. Draftsmen who make detail drawings from layouts are *detailers.*

Assembly drawings are made to show the relationship of one part to another in a machine. They also serve as a check on interferences of moving parts. Minor details and dimensions are omitted; some assembly drawings are in outline form. Assembly drawings serve for erection or assembly of machines in the shop where they are made or where they are to be used. Only such dimensions as are needed for installation or erection are given. Assembly drawings also serve in selling the machine through proposals and catalogs. Drawings for catalogs may show the over-all size to help determine the floor space and clearance necessary for the machine.

The drafting department is required to turn out drawings that are dependable. These drawings must be clear in meaning. The exact shape must be shown, with accurate dimensions, notes, and specifications. The workmanship of the draw-

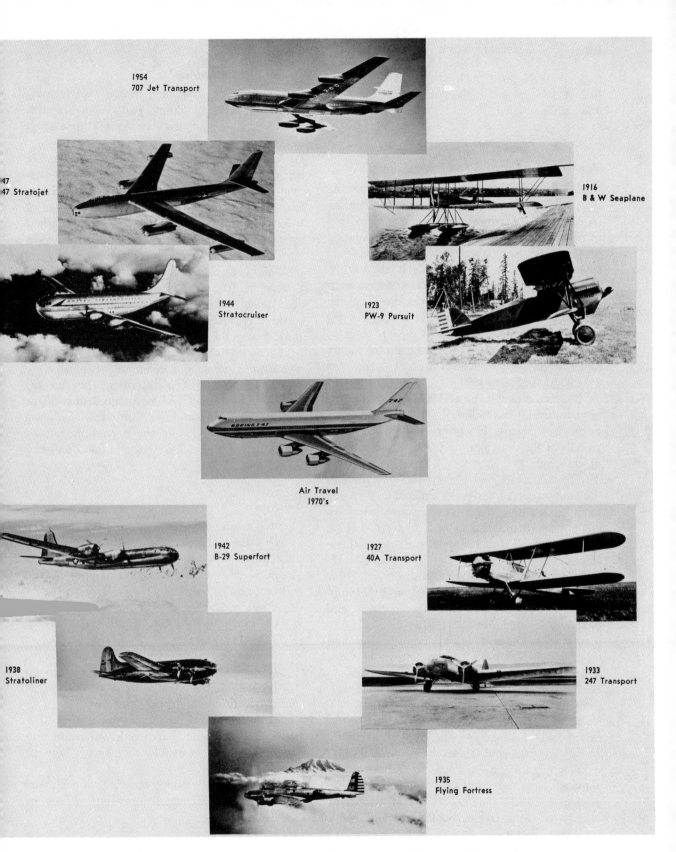

Fig. 115A. Design Evolution of the Airplane (Courtesy, The Boeing Company)
Air Travel 1970's

ings should express such clarity and accuracy that it will inspire high-class workmanship in making the product.

Education of Engineers

A bachelor's degree in engineering representing four years of college education is the minimum requirement for employment as a professional mechanical engineer. High school mathematics, physics, and mechanical drawing are basic to college preparation in mechanical engineering. The average starting salary for a mechanical engineer in 1966 was $8,300 per year. More advanced education brings more money. It is common for an engineer with a master's degree to start at $9,500 to $10,000 per year. A beginning salary range for an engineer with a doctor's degree was $11,000 to $14,500 in 1966.[3]

Draftsmen may be trained in school or through apprenticeship in industry. Apprentices often begin by making blueprints and maintaining records of the drawings, and then to the making of drawings.

The work of an engineer is required all through the long process of designing a machine, planning for its production, and its actual construction. An engineer must understand how to read working drawings of all kinds and how to make them, since drafting is the language of the engineer. He must understand how mechanisms work, how machine operations are performed, and the properties of materials. He must have vision and imagination.

He must know the qualities of metals and other materials. He must know something about their strength, their weight, their reaction to heat and cold; even the results of hammering, drawing, and bending them.

Engineers constantly use mathematics in figuring data of all kinds: size, weight, strength, cost of material, and labor.

The engineer must know something about standard tools, parts and sizes; such as fasteners, appliances, drills, reamers. He must also know how to use catalogs, handbooks, and data sheets.

Opportunities in Drafting

A beginning draftsman who is able to make detail drawings of simple parts from assembly drawings under supervision receives an average wage of $370.00 per month.[4]

A man with good training and considerable experience usually becomes a competent draftsman and is able to make layouts of machines from the designers' sketches, detail drawings of the more complicated parts, and well finished assembly drawings. A competent man works largely under his own direction, cooperates fully with the organization of the drafting room, and is dependable. Such a draftsman in 1966 received an average salary of $580.00 per month.[5] Architectural draftsmen are paid about the same as draftsmen in the engineering field.

Chief engineers, experimental engineers, designing engineers, and chief draftsmen all have special duties and responsibilities. They are the most highly trained and experienced men in the engineering division of a large manufacturing organization. They also are among the highest paid; their individual salaries run into thousands of dollars.

Questions

1. A machine is really a tool to do work. (True or False)
2. The chief work of a mechanical engineer is to design or construct machines. (True or False)
3. Catalog drawings show the floor space and clearance necessary to install the machine. (True or False)
4. Many ideas are submitted for new designs of machines, but they have to be given up because of poor design or because the cost would be too high. (True or False)
5. A committee of engineers decides whether a device is one that people will want and if it will be possible to make. (True or False)
6. Dimensioned working drawings of each part are known as detail drawings. (True or False)

[3]*Ibid.*
[4]*Ibid.*

[5]*Ibid.*

Engineering and Art

There is much art and design in connection with modern mechanical engineering. It is difficult to consider the work of the mechanical engineer without emphasizing that his work today cannot well be successful without an understanding of the importance of making things beautiful.

Modern streamlining is an example of the influence of the industrial artist. Compare the early airplanes with the modern ones; the first automobiles and those now in use; the early washing machines and the latest ones; the early cameras and the new ones; the old bicycles and the new ones, and you will understand how the industrial artists have helped to make modern products more useful and beautiful.

With the many changes in machine production have come the artist's changes that have made the many new things so pleasing in design. The work of the industrial artist is necessary today in every phase of industrial and commercial activity. Have you seen the old corner grocery store with its old show cases and its complication of goods piled here and there without thought to appearance? Then, as you walk into a modern store, observe how much attention is given to design of equipment and packages and artistic display of goods.

Training and Employment

In 1965 about 10,000 industrial designers held positions in industry or did free-lance designing. It is expected that the numbers needed and employed will be on the increase in the next decade. Starting salaries for beginners in industrial design were $400 to $500 per month in 1964.[1] There is

[1]Bureau of Labor Statistics, U.S. Department of Labor: Washington, D.C., 1968-69. Bulletin No. 1550.

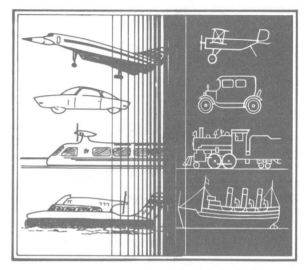

Fig. 116. Comparing the Early with the Modern
(Courtesy, General Motors Company)

Fig. 117. 1909 Automobile

Fig. 118. Recent Model Automobile

considerable variation in the salaries in relation to the work responsibilities and the type of designing being done. Experienced designers earn from $8,000 to $25,000 annually. A few designers are known to make more than $200,000 annually.

There is opportunity for young people to become industrial designers, and it is very interesting work. If you like art and drafting and shop subjects, you may have the qualities that would be necessary to become an artist in industry. When taking art, drafting and shopwork, it would be well for you to talk with your teachers about the opportunities for training and securing employment in designing industrial products.

There are large concerns that are owned and directed by leading master industrial artists. These organizations are constantly working with engineers in designing newer and more beautiful things. And there must be young people willing to take the training that will prepare them for places of opportunity that are sure to be available in modern industrial designing.

Fig. 119. First Folding Camera — 1890
(Courtesy, Eastman Kodak Company)

Fig. 120. Recent Model Camera
(Courtesy, Eastman Kodak Company)

Producing from the Drawing

It is of value for the draftsman to know the practices of the production shops in order that his drawings will be practical. It is also interesting to know what happens to the drawings after they are sent to the shops. A few descriptions of common machines and operations are given in this lesson. However, as a student of drawing, you should take courses in patternmaking, foundry practice, and machine shop. At least, you should visit such shops and study the methods of work.

Any of the jobs that require castings in their making, and that are drawn in the drafting room, must go through three shops: the *pattern shop*, the *foundry*, and the *machine shop*.

Patternmaking

The drawing goes to the pattern shop where craftsmen make exact models, or *patterns*, with wood or metal. The models are used in the making of *sand molds* in the foundry, Fig. 121. The impression made in the sand with the pattern is filled with molten iron. When the iron (or any other metal being used) cools, it shrinks. Therefore, for measuring in the pattern shop, a special rule called a *shrink rule* is used. It looks exactly like a common rule, but the graduations are changed to account for the shrinkage in the casting. So, by using the shrink rule for measuring, the *casting* when cooled is the size called for in the drawing with allowance made for any necessary machining.

Patterns are made of wood and metal. Metal is used in making some patterns, especially when numerous molds are to be made. The operations used by the craftsman in making wood patterns are quite the same as those used by the skilled woodworker. The patternmaker must work very accurately. In the automobile industry, a kind of work closely resembling patternmaking is that of modelmaking. In many cases, the body and wheels are made of wood to full size. This is done so that the design can more easily be studied.

When a pattern is made, there must be allowance for machining. *Draft* must also be allowed. The draft is a sloping of the sides of the pattern so it can be withdrawn from the mold. Webs, lugs, holes, and other details of the finished project must be provided in making the pattern.

Patterns that are symmetrically shaped are made in two parts for ease in molding. They are called *split patterns* and are held together in the mold with dowels, Fig. 121. All of the pattern is properly shaped. Even the small rounded inside corners, or *fillets*, called for in the drawing are made in the pattern.

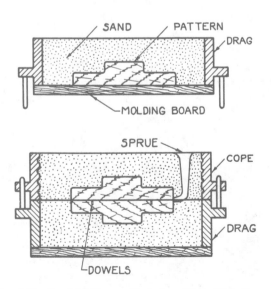

Fig. 121. Sand Molds are Made in a Flask. This Shows a Split Pattern in Place

Foundry Work

The pattern is sent to the foundry for molding and for making a casting. In the foundry a mold from the pattern is made in moist sand. Since the depression in the sand is only of the outside shape of the part to be cast, cores of baked sand and linseed oil are formed and placed in position in the mold to provide for the larger hollow portions in the casting. A funnel-shaped hole, or sprue, and a channel, or gate, leading to the depression or mold are provided. When all is ready, the molten metal which has been melted in a *cupola* is poured into the mold from ladles.

It is common practice to cast many small parts, such as knobs, carburetor bodies, oil burner float valve bodies, ice skates, external bolt threads, small gears, and even golf balls by the die-casting method, Fig. 122. As the term implies, the part is cast in a *die*. A die is a reusable metal form.

To form the mold in the die, instead of making a split pattern of the part with its coreprints and cores, the shape of the part with draft and rounded corners is cut into a mating steel block. When the blocks are placed in position, a hollow space, the shape of the part to be cast, is formed. This space resembles the mold in sand after the pattern has been removed and the *cope* is replaced on the *drag*. As in sand molding cores, vents to let out the air and gates to allow the molten metal to flow into the mold must be provided. Provision for cooling or heating certain parts of the die must be made to permit the metal to flow uniformly to all parts of the die.

Die casting has greatly developed in the last decade and has been made possible largely because tin and lead, zinc, aluminum, and magnesium alloys have been perfected. Dies and cores that are made of the better steel which is now available are long lasting and can be used over and over again, and rapidly, in a machine. Complicated parts now can easily be cast in this way. Fully automatic dies are successfully used to produce a large variety of parts in great numbers. Valve bodies and carburetor parts can be cast at the rate of two a minute. Semi-automatic and even hand-operated machines have high-production possibilities.

Fig. 122. A Modern Die-Casting Machine (Courtesy, Kux Machine Company)

The Machine Shop

One of the most common of the finishing processes on castings is done by either the *planer* or the *shaper* in the machine shop, Fig. 123. The planer is used on heavy castings and the shaper is used on light castings. Either of these machines planes the surface smooth and flat, as indicated by the finish marks on the drawing. The casting is clamped to the bed of the machine. If the planer is used, the casting moves to the cutter, but if the shaper is used, the cutter moves to the casting, Fig. 124. Once the cutter is set on either machine and the machine is put into operation, the work proceeds automatically.

The *milling machine,* Fig. 125, is used for planing all kinds of surfaces. Spirals, tapers, gears, key seats, and slots are cut on the milling machine as readily as are curved surfaces. A variety of cutters can be used so that most any type of surface can be smoothed.

Grinding of many kinds may be necessary in following directions of a drawing for completion of a casting, Fig. 126. On the *grinder* an abrasive grinding wheel revolves on a shaft, or arbor, and rough castings may be smoothed on it. Grinders with special wheels are used

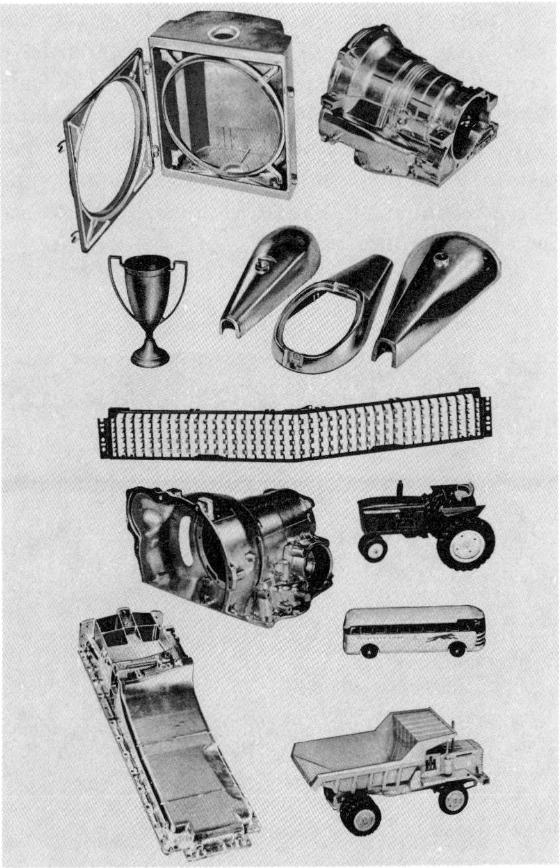

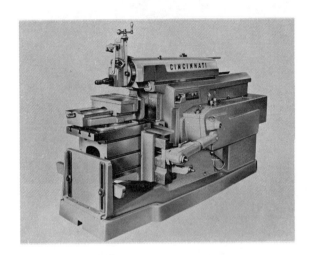

Fig. 123. Shaper (Courtesy, Cincinnati Shaper Company)

Fig. 122A. Plastic Products Produced by a Die-Casting Machine

Fig. 124. Milling Machine (Courtesy, The Cincinnati Milling Machine Company)

to finish and polish. Cutting tools are also sharpened on the grinder.

The *lathe* is used for turning cylindrical pieces, Fig. 127. Boring holes and tapering and threading are also done on the lathe. There are usually more lathes than other machines in a machine shop.

The *drill press* is used for drilling holes. There are different kinds of drill presses, such as the common wall, floor, and radial types. One or several holes can be drilled or bored at the same time. On the radial drill press, holes can be bored at an angle. Holes up to 2″ in diameter may be drilled. Threaded holes of small size are drilled before they are tapped.

The numerically controlled drill press, Fig. 128, may be compared to the player piano in its operation. Both devices have a roll of paper with holes punched at various locations to control the working mechanism. The machine performs the predetermined and repetitious operations precisely as programmed. Early methods of cutting or drilling by template meant tedious and time-consuming setups, but numerical control automates the operations.

Taps and *dies* are used in cutting threads. The tap is used to cut threads in holes that have been drilled. Dies are used for cutting outside threads up to 1″ in diameter on rods to form bolts and other threaded parts. Taps and dies also are used to cut common threads and pipe threads. Square threads and special threads are cut on the lathe.

Fig. 125. Milling Machine
(Courtesy, Cincinnati Milling Machine Company)

Fig. 126. Grinder
(Courtesy, Brown and Sharpe Manufacturing Company)

Fig. 127. Modern Machine Shop for
Aerospace Production (Courtesy Clausing)

Forming Sheet Metal

Metal parts also are formed from sheet metal by means of *forming dies.* Axle housings, gear housings, radiator grills, fenders, automobile bodies, and a great many other parts used every day are pressed into shape from heavy sheet steel by means of dies mounted in great presses, Fig. 129. Mating dies are formed in the toolrooms with great precision so that the face of one exactly matches the face of the other.

While the dies are drawn apart in the press, the sheet metal is inserted in the opening and then the dies are brought together under enormous pressure. The dies again are separated and the form is removed. To make some forms it may be necessary to blank the stock for the form first, then form it into shape, and finally trim the waste from the edges. Blanking, forming, drawing, and trimming dies are easily made to all sorts of shapes in automatic machines.

Fig. 128. Numerically Controlled Drill Press (Courtesy, Aluminum Company of America)

Fig. 129. Punch Press for Forming Body Parts of Automobiles (Courtesy, Fisher Body, Div. General Motors Corporation)

There are many other tools and operations involved in completing the work on metal parts. However, the more common tasks that craftsmen perform after the drawing goes to the shop have been given.

In Fig. 130 a computer programmer is preparing a production setup for a milling machine. Use of automatic planning and control devices is increasing in large industries.

Fig. 130. Computer Programmer at Work (Courtesy, The Cincinnati Milling Machine Company)

Testing for accuracy is necessary throughout the production process, Fig. 131A. Work may be highly finished, but if it is inaccurate it would be of little value. There are various testing devices of which the micrometer is most used. There also are gages, scales, calipers, squares, and straightedges of various kinds.

In Fig. 131B a NASA technician at the Goddard Spacecenter in California tests and rechecks an ionosphere explorer at every level of production as well as in final checking of drawings.

The Electronic Computer

The electronic computer is one of the fascinating developments of the technological age. It is a machine that can make mathematical calculations at unusual speeds and can store multitudes of ideas for quick reproduction in an endless number of human activities, such as:

1. Processing of inventories
2. Banking
3. Controlling machine operations in mass production
4. Making weather forecasts
5. Precooked foods research
6. Evaluation of medical records and diagnosis
7. Analyzing air traffic
8. Legal research
9. Research in various aspects of automobile and aircraft design and manufacture

Fig. 131A. Computers were Involved in the Manufacture of Airplanes (Courtesy, Douglas Aircraft Corporation)

Fig. 131B. NASA Technician Checks the Ionosphere Explorer During Environmental Tests (Courtesy, NASA)

10. Control of missiles
11. Criminal detection and apprehension

A Time and Labor Saver

The computer will do work that would be too slow and laborious if done by a great number of people. It is efficient and fast; therefore, it is growing in use in business and in manufacturing.

In the production of automobiles, the potential use of computers is endless. For example, engineers have found that the computer reduces the man-hours necessary in design of cams from 25 man-hours down to 1 hour. Sketching and providing drafting data are accurately accomplished by the *Orthomat* computer, Fig. 131C.

Some machine tools are numerically controlled, Fig. 128, using computer functions. The instructions are usually recorded on tape. After the tapes have been used, they may be filed for future use. When the computer is used to control production, it can make thousands of accurate reproductions in quantity.

The computer is also used in the work of the Atomic Energy Commission in discovering potential uses of atomic energy. This work is usually done under contract with universities and industries. At the University of California there is research underway which includes peaceful as well as military uses of atomic energy.

The Department of Defense utilizes computers in its many operations in relation to supplies, communications, research, and development. Computers are used by the National Aeronautics Space Administration in preparation, launching, and control of spacecraft. It is said that the space operations would be quite impossible without computers. They are used in design, development testing, preflight checking, launching, control and stabilization, navigation, reentry, and recovery of spacecraft. The Gemini spacecraft, Fig. 113, has a computer that provides the astronauts with assistance in many of its maneuvers at the rate of 7000 calculations per second while it travels through space faster than 17,000 miles per hour.

The foregoing are just a few of the hundreds of possible uses for the computer. Many more are being investigated. There are many kinds of computers, but all essentially do intricate work and speed up operations. Each type of computer has its special advantages. Every problem solved by the computer involves facts provided by people who are experts in their special fields of work.

People and the Computer

Persons who prepare the questions and answers for the computer are called *systems analysts* and *programmers*. The total activity of "make-ready" for the computer is called *programming*. The analyst or programmer has the responsibility of preparing the coded information or *input* for the machine. The solution from the machine is called

Fig. 131C.   The Orthomat is a Numerically Controlled Drafting Machine (Courtesy, Universal Drafting Machine Corporation)

Fig. 131D.   Training for Computer Programming (Courtesy, Stout State University)

output. Programming is often laborious, but it results in the fast completion of work done with consistent accuracy.

The information provided may be in various forms, depending upon the work and kind of computer involved. Punched cards, punched paper rolls, magnetic tapes, magnetic drums, magnetic cores, and magnetic discs are among the many devices used to store information for computers. Language is too cumbersome for speedy machines, so it must be converted into machine code. An artificial, abbreviated language must be used; only a certain code can be used in a certain computer. The United States of America Standards Institute is considering the possibility of a uniform code which is likely to result in a standard type of computer language; however, some engineers doubt this possibility.

Training

Training for the work of programming is not complex. It is not necessary for the programmer to know how the computer works any more than the driver of an automobile needs to know how the motor of his car works. A mathematics background is not usually necessary. In some instances, the skill of a programmer need not be greater than that of a skilled typist. High school students can learn to do programming. Good general intelligence, willingness to attend to details, accuracy, and patience and persistence are attributes of a successful programmer. A college education in engineering and scientific work in a good many fields is desirable, and the college-educated man or woman has endless opportunities for advancement. The demand for such workers far exceeds the supply, and for many years this need will increase.

Training for computer programming is provided by educational institutions and the manufacturers of computers, Fig. 131D. Eventually, information about computers and their many uses may be taught in the elementary schools, because the computer will probably become a way of life as is the automobile, radio, and television.

Opportunities for Employment

Information on employment of programmers

2*Ibid.*

in the United States is not adequate, but it may be estimated that in 1966 there were 100,000 programmers employed. This number includes full-time programmers as well as part-time engineers, scientists, economists, accountants, and other workers who require special training related to computer programming. Most employment at present is with the larger business organizations and the government.

For the next 10 years many thousands of jobs will be available to trained programmers. College-trained people with at least 2 years beyond high school and a background in science, mathematics, or vocational-technical experience will be much in demand. Most workers now are young, and the opportunities for advancement are increasing. Draftsmen have an exceedingly important role along with the engineers in preparing blueprints for construction of computers, and computers will be utilized in preparing data and drawings. Men highly trained in electronics repair will be in much demand for maintenance of computer equipment.

In 1967 the yearly salaries for beginners averaged $7,300 to $11,000 for experienced programmers in 2000 business organizations; supervisory personnel averaged $17,550 a year. Working conditions are excellent, and the fringe benefits are as favorable as for other highly technical occupations.[2]

Questions

1. Give the names, in proper order, of the shops through which a job is produced from a drawing.
2. Give in more detail than is explained in this lesson, the operations involved in production in each shop named in question one.
3. Name other machines and tools than those mentioned in this lesson.
4. What is a computer, and what is its purpose?
5. Name ten areas of work in which computers are used.
6. What is the meaning of input, and who prepares it? What is output?
7. What is the language of the computer?
8. Can it be assumed that engineering education includes study of the computer?
9. What are the future opportunities for employment in programming?

Metals in Manufacture

If one were to tell about the history and the production of metals of various kinds, it would be necessary to start with iron and consider it with its various modifications. Iron and its many forms is the most used of the metals. These are known as *ferrous metals* and may be placed into three general classes: cast iron, wrought iron, and steel.

Nearly all of the objects drawn in machine drawing are produced in some form of the ferrous metals; therefore, it would be interesting to know something about these metals.

There seems to be no record available that tells when iron was first produced. It is known that the Egyptians, Greeks, Hebrews, and Romans were familiar with its use. The Romans are credited with starting its manufacture in England during the Roman occupation.

The first methods of producing iron were crude compared with the methods used today. However, in the early days, just as now, the process consisted of placing iron ore, as taken from the mines, in furnaces and heating or *smelting* it. Oxygen is liberated from the ore by the intense heat, leaving the raw or pig iron from which other forms of iron and steel are made. The furnaces used today have been brought to a very high standard of perfection.

Iron ore is mined in two major areas in the United States. These areas are in the region around Lake Superior and in Alabama. About eighty per cent of the ore mined comes from the Lake Superior District.

Considerable chemistry is involved in the production of metals. It is a form of chemical engineering known as *metallurgy*. All metals are defined, studied, and improved for special uses by means of chemical analysis. It is said that this branch of chemical engineering offers many opportunities for young men who are interested in such work.

The production of the various forms of ferrous metals that are now available requires many different and complicated processes and types of furnaces.

Ferrous Metals

Pig iron, the first product in the smelting process, is more or less impure. The commercially pure form obtained from pig iron is called wrought iron. It contains a small percentage of carbon. An increase in the amount of carbon content in the pig iron over the amount necessary in wrought iron gives mild steel. In fact, wrought iron is really a low-carbon steel. Up to a certain point, increase of carbon content in the mild steel produces tool steel. Cast iron, however, is produced when the carbon content is increased beyond the amount needed for tool steel. The carbon content of cast iron ranges usually from about 3 per cent to as high as 4.8 per cent.

Cast iron is made into various products by pouring molten pig iron, heated in a cupola, into molds of the desired shape of the products. Cast iron is hard, but brittle, and it breaks easily. It is used a great deal because it can be poured into molds and made into desired shapes. The products made by pouring the molten iron into molds are called castings. Cast iron is also made malleable or pliable by a special annealing process before casting. Malleable iron resists shock better than does cast iron.

Wrought iron cannot be cast, but it is tougher than cast iron. Steel can be cast but only at very high temperature, and it is a difficult process. Wrought iron and steel are usually formed into desired shapes by forging, rolling, or pressing. Steel is harder and stronger than iron. The amount of carbon in the steel determines its hardness, as well as its use. For instance, different grades of steel are used in making tools, machines, springs, and rails.

It is said that about 21 per cent of all the steel used goes into the construction industry; 11 per cent goes into railroads; 8½ per cent into containers, such as tin cans; 4 per cent is used on the farm; 5 per cent goes into machinery. The remainder goes into a variety of things.

Alloys

An *alloy* is formed by combining two or more metals. Special forms of steel are alloys. Brass, solder, bronze, and babbitt are also alloys.

Special steels, used for high speed cutting tools, and stainless steels are alloys. Some of the common steel alloys are steel and nickel, steel and tungsten, steel and chromium, and steel and vanadium. Brass is a combination of copper and zinc; solder is composed of lead and tin; bronze is formed with copper and tin; babbitt is produced with copper, tin, and antimony. A light metal used in aeronautical manufacturing is called *duralumin*. It is strong and light in weight.

Some Metal Projects

A list of a few metal products and the kinds of metal used in them would be interesting and helpful to the draftsman. A few products of the common metals are listed below:

Pig iron — other iron and steel.

Cast iron — stove parts, machine frames, radiators, water and sewer pipes, grilles, light fixtures.

Malleable cast iron — pipe fittings, cheap tools, stoves.

Wrought iron — bolts in boiler construction.

Steel of low-carbon content — bolts, shafts, frames, grilles.

Steel of medium-carbon content — structural steel.

Steel of high-carbon content — keen cutting tools.

Copper — rivets, wire, water pipes, flashing.

Bronze — bearings, bushings, statuary, bells.

---

[1]Bureau of Labor Statistics, U.S. Department of Labor: Washington, D.C., 1968-69. Bulletin No. 1550.

Brass — screws, pipes, door plates, musical instruments, light fixtures.

Lead — battery parts, pipes, shot.

Tin — utensils, such as cups, plates, pans, tin foil, plating.

Aluminum — cooking utensils, grilles.

There are many metals and metal products, but the machine draftsman needs only to know about the metals used most commonly in the field of activity for which he makes drawings. A knowledge of metallurgy is necessary for those who design metal products. Improvement in metals and economy in costs are made possible through metallurgical science.

Education and Opportunities

Training for more than 1000 different types of occupations in the iron and steel industries is usually on-the-job training with formal schooling offered in related technical fields such as chemistry, physics, and metallurgy. Advancement is based on technical skill and know-how. Thousands of workers will be employed during the next decade. High school graduates are preferred when beginners are selected in the various occupational categories. Opportunities for advancement to the more technical occupations will be certain, while there is likely to be a gradual decline in routine, unskilled jobs. There will be a growing need for chemists, physicists, mathematicians, electronic technicians, electronic computer programmers, laboratory aides, and instrument repairmen because of the increasing complexity of machines in use.[1] The wages of iron and steel workers paid in 1965 were $3.43 per hour. This wage rate was among the highest hourly wage of the manufacturing occupations.

Questions

1. Name a few metal products other than those listed.
2. Name several stainless steel products.
3. Little is known regarding the beginnings of iron production. (True or False)
4. Iron ore is mined in two areas in the United States. They are in the regions near Lake Superior and in Alabama. (True or False)
5. Wrought iron is a form of (A).
6. The amount of (A) in steel determines its hardness.

Sketching Arcs and Circles

It is often necessary to make sketches of cylindrical objects. With a little care and patience you can easily learn to make a very good free-hand sketch of a circle.

1. To locate the center of the circle, sketch a horizontal and a vertical center line, Fig. 132.

2. On the horizontal center line, to the right and to the left of the center, mark off a distance equal to the radius of the desired circle. On the vertical center line, above and below the center, mark off distances equal to the radius, Fig. 133.

3. Draw fine lines at 45° to the horizontal, Fig. 134. When enough skill has been gained in sketching circles, the 45° center lines may be omitted. In sketching small circles these lines *are never drawn*.

4. From the center, mark off distances on the 45° lines equal to the radius, Fig. 135. Train the eye to locate the points equally distant from the center as accurately as possible. This can be done easily with practice.

5. Lightly sketch the upper left quarter of the circle, Fig. 136. Keep the arc quite full and round; it should meet the center lines squarely.

6. With equal care and using a light line, sketch the lower left quarter, Fig. 137.

7. In the same manner sketch the upper right quarter, Fig. 138, and the lower right quarter, Fig. 139.

8. Examine the work carefully. True up the circumference wherever needed. Make the circle smooth and true. Darken the line.

Fig. 132. Sketching Circle, First Step

Fig. 133. Sketching Circle, Second Step

Fig. 134. Sketching Circle, Third Step

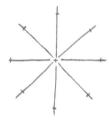

Fig. 135. Sketching Circle, Fourth Step

Fig. 136. Sketching Circle, Fifth Step

Fig. 137. Sketching Circle, Sixth Step

Fig. 138. Sketching Circle, Seventh Step

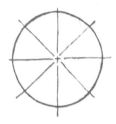

Fig. 139. Completed Circle

Drawing Arcs and Circles

Arcs and circles are drawn with the compasses. See Figs. 140 and 143. If the radius is less than ¾″, the spring bow compasses are used, Fig. 141. Center lines must first be laid out for properly locating the centers for arcs or circles.

1. On fine sandpaper, dress the lead in the compasses to a bevel point as shown in Fig. 142.
2. See that the lead is slightly softer than the lead in the drawing pencil you are using. For example, if you are using a *4H* pencil for the straight lines, a *3H* lead would be used in the compasses.
3. Adjust the needle point *A*, Fig. 141, so it is slightly longer than the lead *B*, Fig. 141. The straight side of the lead should face toward the opposite leg, the bevel out, to make a sharp line for a large circle.

In order to ink with the large compasses, the leg containing the lead must be replaced with the pen. See *A*, Fig. 140. Be careful in taking instruments apart. They are very easily damaged.

4. With the scale, lay off the radius to the desired dimension on scrap paper. Set the compasses to this distance.
5. Hold the compasses, as shown in Figs. 143 and 147, with the handle between the thumb and first finger.
6. With the little finger of the left hand as a guide, Fig. 144, place the needle point exactly and lightly on the center lines for the desired circle or arc. Allow only the weight of the compasses to bear on the needle

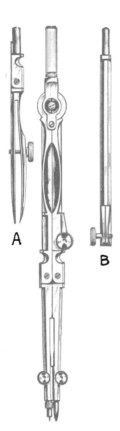

Fig. 140.   Combination Ink Pen and Pencil Compasses

Fig. 141. Bow Pencil

Fig. 142.   Dress the Lead
to a Bevel Point

104

point so that only a trace of the center mark will remain when the line has been made.

7. Revolve the compasses to the right and at the same time tip them forward slightly as shown in Figs. 143 and 147.

8. To draw a circle larger than three inches in diameter, bend the legs of the compasses at the joints so the legs will be perpendicular to the paper, Fig. 145.

9. To draw circles larger than ten inches in diameter, attach the lengthening bar, *B*, Fig. 140, and adjust the legs to position as shown in Fig. 146. Hold the compasses by the legs rather than by the handle when making the larger circles.

10. To make small arcs and circles, use the bow pencil. See Figs. 141 and 147. The needle point and lead are adjusted in the same manner as for the large compasses. The bow pencil is held and used in the same way as are the large compasses.

11. While turning the nut to adjust the bow pencil, press the legs together to release the pressure on the threads. The threads

Fig. 144. With the Little Finger as a Guide, Place the Needle Point Lightly for Location of Center

Fig. 143. Hold the Compasses Between the Thumb and the First Finger and Tip them Forward as the Line is Made

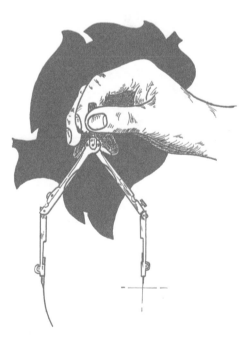

Fig. 145. Drawing a Circle Larger than Three Inches Diameter

are so fine they are easily worn unless used only to hold the legs in position and for fine adjustment.

Questions

1. Why is it advisable to use lead in the compasses slightly softer than the lead in the drawing pencil?
2. In order to make the line in a circle darker, it is advisable to retrace by going back and forth with the compasses. (True or False)
3. The holes left by the needle point of the compasses should be seen only by careful inspection. (True or False)

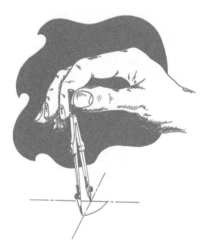

Fig. 147. Drawing a Small Circle

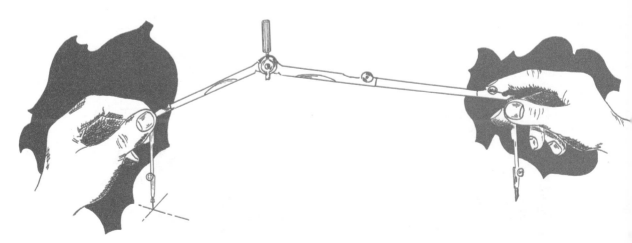

Fig. 146. Use the Extension Bar When Inking Large Circles

PROBLEMS

Required: Working drawings of cylindrical objects

Problem 1: Wooden Wheel

Data:
Diameter, 4½″
Thickness, ¾″
Diameter of hole, ¾″

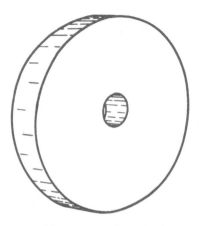

Problem 1 — Wooden Wheel

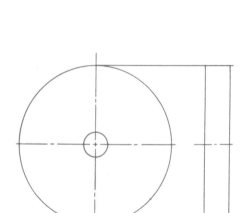

Step 1

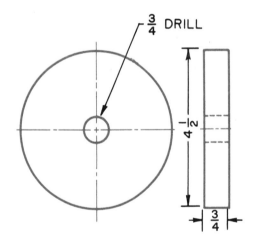

Step 2

Problem 2: Ink Bottle Holder

Data:
Outside diameter, 3¾″
Diameter of hole, 2″
Depth, ⅝″
Thickness, 1″
Chamfer, ¼″ x 45°

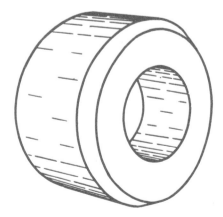

Problem 2 — Ink Bottle Holder

Problem 3: Collar

Data:

Large diameter, (A) 3¼″
Small outside diameter, (B) 2⅛″
Thickness at large diameter, (C) 1¼″
Diameter of hole, (D) 1⅜″
Over-all length, (E) 5¼″
Bevel, (F) ¼″ x 45°

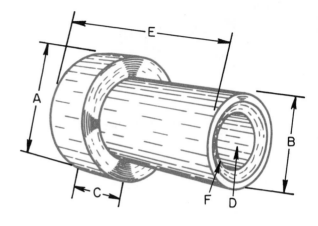

Problem 3 — Collar

Problem 4: Eccentric

Data:

Large diameter, 2.25″
Small outside diameter, 1.5″
Length of shaft, 3.5″
Over-all length, 5″
Diameter of shaft hole, 8.75″
Diameter of small hole, .1875″
Eccentricity, .375″ (difference between centers)
FAO, finish 63

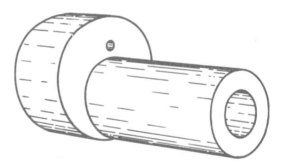

Problem 4 — Eccentric

Problem 5: Cross Link

Data:

Distance of center line of top hole from surface X, 1¾″
Distance of center line of side hole from surface X, 1″
Diameter of holes, .5″
Radius of each end, 1″
Thickness of surfaces through which holes are drilled, 1″
Thickness of surface Y, ¾″

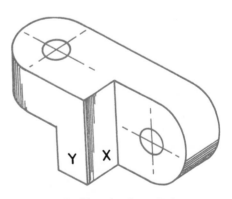

Problem 5 — Cross Link

Problem 6: Hanger Clamp

Data:

Sleeve, 4″ long x 2″d
Inside diameter of sleeve, 1¼″
Width of slot, ³⁄₁₆″
Diameter of holes, .625″
Lugs, ⅜″ thick, ⅝″ radius
Distance from centers of sleeve to centers of
 lug holes, 2⅜″
Spacing of lugs, ⁷⁄₁₆″ centered
Width of lugs, 2 times the radius
Fillets, ⅛″ radius

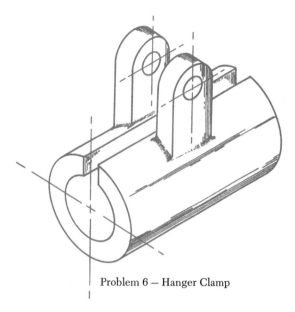

Problem 6 — Hanger Clamp

Problem 7: Bearing Cover

Data:

A = 1.3125″ radius
B = .75″ radius
C = 2.5625″
D = 1″
E = .375″ radius
F = .125″
G = Drill .375″ hole located .5″ from base to
 center
H = 3″
Material, aluminum alloy
FAO, finish 32

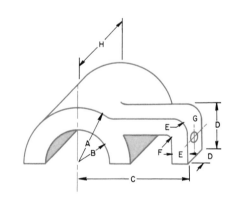

Problem 7 — Bearing Cover

Problem 8: Bracket and Guide

Make a working drawing with dimensions in
 decimals.

Data:

A = 4¼″
B = 2⅛″
C = 3″
D = ⅝″
E = ⅜″
F = ¾″
G = 1″
H = ½″
I = 1½″
J = 1¼″
K = .5″ drill 2 holes
Material, aluminum
FAO, finish 63

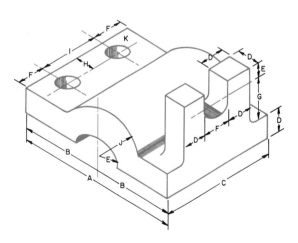

Problem 8 — Bracket and Guide

Problem 9: Offset Base

    Data:

A = 3″

B = 2.625″

C = 4.750″

D = .375″

E = ½″ drill 2 holes

F = .875″

G = .750″ radius

H = .625″ dia.

I = .625″ dia.

J = 1.5″

K = .625″

L = 1.3125″

M= .500″

N = 1.625″

Fillet, ⅛″

Material, steel

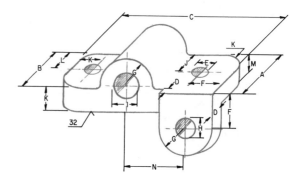

Problem 9 — Offset Base

Drawing
Tangent Lines and Arcs

Here are several constructions that occur often in all kinds of drawings. When a straight line touches an arc so that both lines become one line at the place where they touch, they are *tangent*. Likewise when two arcs touch each other so that the two lines become one at the point of contact, they also are *tangent*.

A line may be tangent to a circle or arc; a circle or arc may be tangent to a line; arcs and circles may be tangent to each other. In Fig. 148 are shown three different views having tangent lines and arcs.

Fillets, Rounds, and Runouts

In machine drafting, the drawing of tangent arcs and lines involves the use of compasses. The terms *fillets, rounds,* and *runouts* are used to describe various applications which have been conventionalized in drafting and in production so that requirements are readily understood.

A *fillet* is an inside curve at the intersection of two surfaces. Castings are designed so that the internal angle will not be sharp. Inside corners are rounded and called fillets as shown in Problem 6, Unit 34 and Problem 7, Unit 40. Fillets add strength to the casting in the mold. A sharp inside corner may crack if the fillet is not provided. The radius of a fillet should be determined by the designer or draftsman. If not indicated, the fillet is usually ⅛″ radius and is made of wax on wood patterns.

Rounds are curves at outside corners as in Problem 7, Unit 40. Corners are usually rounded for appearance as well as for some measure of strength and safety. The radius may be less than ⅛″ or just enough to take off the sharpness. It may be an amount equal to the thickness of the part.

A *runout* is similar to a fillet where two parts intersect as at the point where a spoke, arm, and a hub come together, Problem 5, Unit 40. Usually, a runout appears where two curved surfaces intersect.

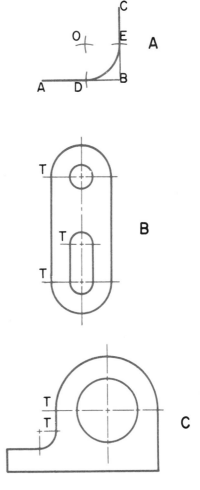

Fig. 148. Tangent Lines and Arcs
"T" shows point of tangency.

Drawing an Arc Tangent to Two Lines at a Right Angle

1. Let *AB* and *BC* be two lines that form a right angle, Fig. 148A.

2. The radius of the arc to be drawn is usually given. With *B* as a center and the compasses set to a radius equal to the size of the desired arc, draw arcs cutting the lines *AB* and *BC* at *D* and *E*.

3. With *D* and *E* as centers, and the same radius, draw the arcs intersecting at *O*.

4. With *O* as a center, with the same radius, draw the desired arc tangent to lines *AB* and *BC* at points *D* and *E*. In Fig. 148C is shown an application of this construction.

Drawing an Arc Tangent to Two Lines Not at a Right Angle

Method A

1. Lines *AB* and *CD* are lines requiring a tangent arc, Fig. 149A.

2. Set the compasses to the radius of the desired arc.

3. With any points on lines *AB* and *CD* as centers, draw the four arcs as shown.

4. Draw lines *A'B'* and *C'D'* tangent to these arcs, thereby making them parallel to lines *AB* and *CD*. The intersection of *A'B'* and *C'D'* at point *O* is the center for the desired arc.

5. With the setting of the compasses unchanged and with *O* as a center, draw the tangent arc.

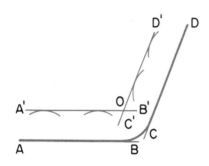

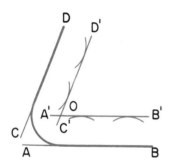

Fig. 149A. Arcs Tangent to Lines not at Right Angles

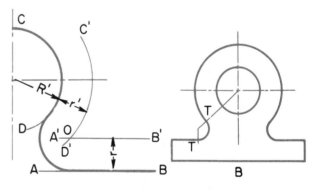

Fig. 150. An Arc Tangent to a Straight Line and a Given Arc

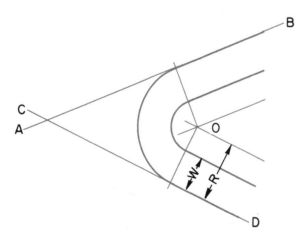

Fig. 149B. Arcs Tangent to Lines not at Right Angles

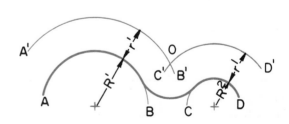

Fig. 151. Tangent Arcs

6. The triangles and the scale can be used in drawing lines *AB* and *CD* parallel to the given lines. See Unit 26.

Method B

1. Lines *AB* and *CD* are lines requiring a tangent arc. See Fig. 149B.
2. *R* is the desired radius.
3. Draw two lines parallel to *AB* and *CD* with *R* distance apart. Where the lines intersect at *O*, locate the center of the arc.
4. Locate the tangent points by drawing lines perpendicular to lines *AB* and *CD* at point *O*.
5. With *R* as a radius and *O* as the center, draw the desired arc.
6. An inner arc, as for the inside curve of a roadway, can be made by drawing a smaller arc with *O* as a center. The width of the roadway would be the desired radius of the inner curve subtracted from the outer curve.

Drawing an Arc Tangent to a Straight Line And a Given Arc

1. Line *AB* and arc *CD* are to be joined by a tangent arc. See *A* in Fig. 150. Let r^1 be the given radius of the desired arc.
2. Draw arc *CD* by setting the compasses to a radius equal to $R^1 + r^1$.
3. Draw line *AB* a distance equal to r^1 from, and parallel to, line *AB*.
4. The arc *CD* intersects line *AB* at *O*.
5. With *O* as a center and with r^1 as a radius, draw the desired arc tangent to the given arc and the straight line. There is an application of this construction in *B* in Fig. 150.

Drawing Tangent Arcs

1. In Fig. 151 arcs *AB* and *CD* require a tangent arc to join them. Let r^1 be the given radius of the desired arc.
2. Set the compasses to a radius equal to $R^1 + r^1$. With *X*, the center of the larger arc, as a center, draw arc *AB*.
3. Set the compasses to a radius equal to $R^2 + r^1$. With *Y*, the center of the second arc, as a center, draw arc *CD*.

4. The newly drawn arcs intersect at *O* to form the center for the desired tangent arc. Point *O* is equidistant from arcs *AB* and *CD*.
5. Set the compasses to radius r^1. With *O* as a center, draw the desired arc. An application of this construction is shown in Fig. 152.

Drawing a Straight Line Tangent to a Given Arc from a Given Point Outside the Arc

Let *AB* be the given arc with center at C. *D* is the given point. See Fig. 153.
1. Connect *D* and *C*.
2. Bisect the distance *DC*, locating *O'* on *DC* by drawing intersecting arcs at *E* and *F*, with centers at *D* and *C* and a radius greater than half of *DC*. A straight line through *E* and *F* locates *O'*, the center of *DC*.

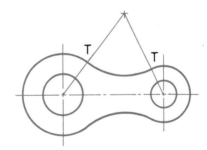

Fig. 152.   Tangent Arcs

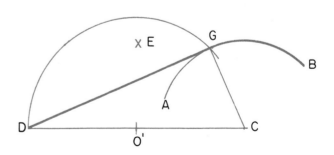

Fig. 153.   Line Tangent to Arc from Point Outside the Arc

3. With $O'D$ as a radius and O' as center, draw the arc DG cutting the given arc AB at G.
4. Draw line DG through D and G and line CG through C and G, completing the right triangle DGC. The line DG is the required tangent and is perpendicular to GC, a radius of the arc AB with center at O'.

NOTE: When the longest side of a triangle is the diameter of a semicircle, the other two sides are perpendicular to each other. Any triangle circumscribed by a semicircle is a right triangle.

Questions

1. How does the distance from any point in the line AB compare with any other point in $A'B'$, Fig. 149A?
2. Likewise, how does the distance from CD of any point in $C'D'$ compare with the distance of any other point from CD, Fig. 149B?
3. Why is O the only point that is equally distant (equidistant) from AB and CD?
4. Study the other constructions in this unit to discover why the construction shown will locate the required center.

PROBLEMS

Problem 1: Magnet

Data:

Outside diameter of head, 3¼″

Distance from center of inside arc to end of arms, 5″

Size of stock, ⅜″ x ⅝″

Total width across arms at the open end, 2″

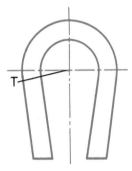

Problem 1 — Magnet

Problem 2: Road Junction

Two divergent roads are to be joined by a road on an arc that will permit a smooth change of direction.

Problem 3: Race Course

Make a diagram for a race course on a triangular plot of ground of approximately the proportions of a 30° - 60° triangle.

Bisecting an Angle

If you had to divide an angle into two equal parts you could do it as follows:

1. Angle *ABC* is to be divided into two equal angles, Fig. 154.
2. With *B* as a center, and with any radius less than *BA*, draw arc *DE*, Fig. 154.
3. With *D* and *E* as centers, and the same radius, draw arcs intersecting at *F*.
4. Draw line *BF* and you will have made two equal angles, *ABF* and *FBC*, Fig. 154.

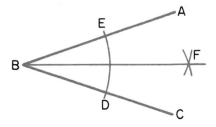

Fig. 154. Bisected Angle

Drawing a Straight Line
Tangent to Two Arcs

This construction will be found very useful when you wish to draw a tangent to two arcs of unequal radii. The following technique would be used to draw the crank in Fig. 163.

1. Let arc *AB* with its center at *O* and arc *CD* with its center at *O* be arcs that require a common tangent, Fig. 155.
2. On *OO'* lay off *BE* equal to *O'D*, the radius of the arc *CD*, giving *OE* the difference between the radii of the two given arcs.
3. With the center at *O* and radius *OE*, draw the arc through *E*.
4. Bisect *OO'* at *F*. See Unit 28.
5. With *OF* as a radius and *F* as a center, draw the arc on *OO'* cutting the arc *GE* at *G*.
6. Draw *OT* through *G*, locating *T*, the point of tangency on the large arc *ATB*.
7. Draw the construction line *GO'*, completing the triangle *OGO'*. This triangle is circum-

scribed by a semicircle. Any triangle circumscribed by a semicircle is a right triangle. This is a geometric fact.

8. Since *OG* is at a right angle (perpendicular) to *GO'*, *OT*, an extension of *OG*, is perpendicular to *GO'*. *TT'* and *OG* are equal by construction; *O'T* is equal and parallel to *GT*, being opposite sides of a rectangle.
9. With *T* as center and *O'G* as radius locate *T'*, the point of tangency on the smaller arc.

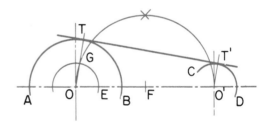

Fig. 155. To Draw a Straight Line to Two Arcs

PROBLEMS

Required: Working drawings of objects that require tangents to be drawn. Your instructor may request that you change the fractional dimensions to decimals as in problem 4.

Problem 1: Link

Data:

Width, 2″

Thickness, ⅝″

Center to center of drilled holes, 5″

Diameter of drilled holes, .625″

Complete the drawing, laying out center lines, circles, and arcs first

Problem 1 — Link

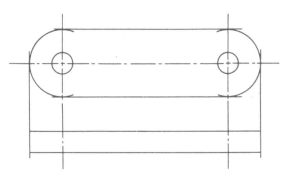

Step 1

Problem 2: Slotted Link

Data:

At one end of the drawing made of the *link* in problem 1, draw a slot ⅝″ wide with a distance of 2″ between the center of the semicircular ends.

Problem 3: Rocker Arm

Data:

Distance between centers, (A) 5½″

Thickness of arm, (B) ½″

Height of bosses above arm, (C) ⅝″

Diameter of bosses, (D) 2¼″

Diameter of holes, (E) 1¼″

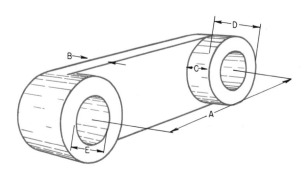

Problem 3 — Rocker Arm

Problem 4: Horizontal Guide

Data:

Base, .75″ x 2.75″ x 7.875″
Bearing or slide, 2.375″ x 2.375″ x 3.75″
Radius of bearing, 1.5″
2 drilled holes, .5″ diameter centered
    1.75″ apart, one concentric with end of base
Radius of fillets at base, .125″

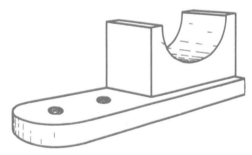

Problem 4 — Horizontal Guide

Problem 5: Link

Data:

Distance between centers, 3⅝″
Diameter of large end, 2¾″
Diameter of large hole, 1¼″
Diameter of small end, 2″
Diameter of small hole, 1″
Height of small cylinder, 2″
Height of large cylinder, 3¼″
Thickness of arm, 1¾″
Radius of arm, 4¼″
Projection of bosses above upper surface of
    arm, ⅛″

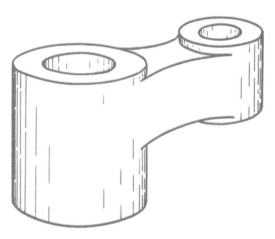

Problem 5 — Link

Problem 6: Rocker Arm

Data:

Distance, center of end holes to center of center
    hole, 3″
Total center-to-center distance, 6″
Outside diameter of center hub, 2⅛″
Inside diameter of center, 1¼″
Outside diameter of ends, 1¼″
Inside diameter of ends, ⅝″
Thickness of hubs, 1¼″ located ³⁄₁₆″ above
    flange and ⁵⁄₁₆″ below
Thickness of flange, ¾″
Radius of fillets, ⅛″
Diameter of centered oil hole on each end,
    ⅛″
Keyway, ⅛″ x ¼″

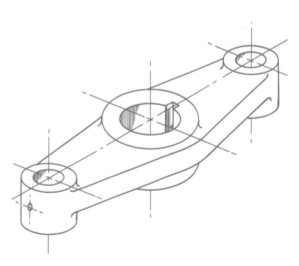

Problem 6 — Rocker Arm

Problem 7: Hinge Fixture

Data:

Distance, center to center, of holes (A) in triangular plate (X), 3¾″

Distance center to center (D), 1⅞″

Diameter of holes, .6875″

Radius of each of three corners of plate, ¹¹⁄₁₆″

Distance from center to center (B) of holes in plate, 2½″

Distance from center line of holes in lugs to center of holes in plate (C), 1½″

Diameter of holes in lugs, .625″

Thickness of lugs, ½″

Distance between lugs, ⅞″

Thickness of plate, ⅝″

Total distance, outside to outside of lugs, 1⅞″

Outside radius of each lug, ⅝″

Distance from center line of lugs to pointed ends of lugs, 3⁵⁄₁₆″

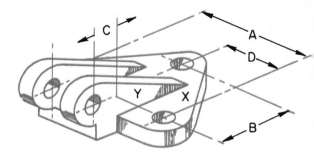

Problem 7 — Hinge Fixture

Problem 8: Shaft Guide

Data:

A = 3″

B = 3.625″

C = 2″

D = .500″

E = 1.500″ dia.

F = .625 drill

G = .750″ radius

H = .625″

I = .4375″ dia.

Material, steel

FAO, finish 63

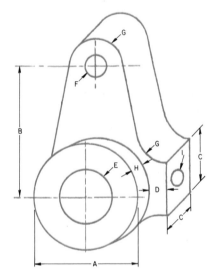

Problem 8 — Shaft Guide

Problem 9: Bracket

Data:

A = 3″

B = 4¾″

C = 2″

D = 1″ dia.

E = 1¾″

F = .5″ drill

G = ½″

Fillets, ⅛″

Material, iron

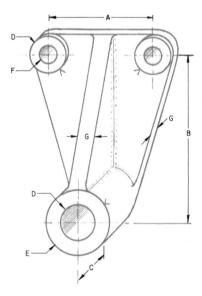

Problem 9 — Bracket

Drawing a Hexagon

A hexagon is a six-sided figure. Its sides and included angles are equal. It is used frequently in mechanical drawing. Many objects in the shops are hexagonal in shape; even your pencil has six sides. Then, too, objects such as hub caps, nuts, bolt heads, special wrenches, and hydrant plugs have hexagonal forms. There are several methods of drawing a hexagon.

With the Long Diameter Given

1. Line *AB* is the long diameter of the desired hexagon, Fig. 156.
2. With the T-square and 30°-60° triangle, draw 30° lines through points *A* and *B* to make lines *AD* and *FB*.
3. Draw 60° lines, *AC*, *AF*, *BD*, and *BE*, from points *A* and *B*. Two of these lines, *AF* and *BD*, will intersect lines *AD* and *BF*.
4. Draw a horizontal line through *D* parallel to *AB* until it intersects line *AC*.
5. Draw line *FE* through point *E* and you will have completed the hexagon.

With One Side Given

1. Let *AB* be a given side, Fig. 157.

2. With *AB* as a radius, with points *A* and *B* as centers, draw the arcs intersecting to form center, *O*.
3. With *O* as a center, and the same radius, draw a circle.
4. With the same radius and starting with point *A* as a center, strike an arc at *F*.
5. With *F* as a center, strike arc *E*; and with *E* as a center, strike arc *D*; and so strike arc *C*.
6. Connect points *BC*, *CD*, *DE*, *EF*, and *FA* and you will have the required hexagon.

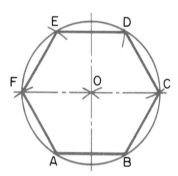

Fig. 157. Hexagon Drawn with One Side Given.
Compasses Method

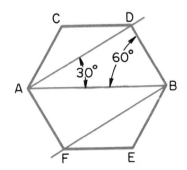

Fig. 156. Hexagon Drawn with the Long Diameter Given

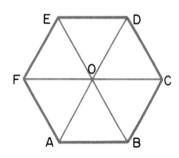

Fig. 158. Hexagon Drawn with One Side Given.
Triangle Method

With One Side Given, Second Method

1. *AB* is the given side, Fig. 158.
2. With a T-square and 30°-60° triangle draw 60° lines *AD* through *A* and *BE* through *B*.
3. Draw line *FC* through *O* and parallel to *AB*.
4. Draw a 60° line through *A* to form line *AF* and through *B* to form *BC*.
5. Draw a 60° line through *F* to form *FE* and through *C* to form *CD*.

6. At the intersection of *EB* and *FE*, draw line *ED* parallel to *AB* to complete the hexagon.

Questions

1. Can you discover other ways to draw regular hexagons? If so, describe.
2. What objects can you name that are hexagonal in shape?

Drawing an Octagon

An octagon is a figure of eight equal sides and angles. It is used much in drawing, but not as frequently as is the hexagon. You will probably see occasional applications of the octagon in woodworking.

With a Square Given

1. Let *A B C D* be the square in which an octagon is to be drawn, Fig. 159.

2. Find the center of the square by drawing the diagonals *AC* and *DB*.

3. Set the compasses to radius *AO*. With *A*, *B*, *C*, and *D* as centers, draw arcs intersect-

ing at points *1* and *4*, *3* and *6*, *5* and *8*, and *7* and *2*.

4. With straight lines, connect *2* and *3*, *4* and *5*, *6* and *7*, and *8* and *1*, and the required octagon will be completed.

With a Square Given, Second Method

1. Draw diagonals *AC* and *DB*, Fig. 160.

2. With *OR* as a radius, draw arcs intersecting the diagonals at *1*, *2*, *3*, and *4*.

3. Through points *1*, *2*, *3*, and *4*, with the 45° triangle, draw lines perpendicular to the diagonals to complete the octagon.

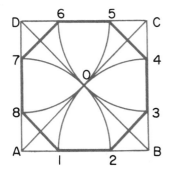

Fig. 159. Octagon Drawn Inside Square with Compasses

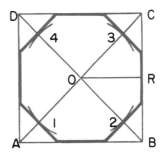

Fig. 160. Octagon Drawn Inside Square with Compasses

PROBLEMS

Required: Working drawings involving hexagons and octagons.

Problem 1: Hexagon Bar

Data:

Width of side and over-all length may be selected by the student or assigned by your instructor.

Problem 2: Plug

Data:
Large diameter, 3¼″
Small diameter, 2¾″
Distance across corners of hexagon end, 2¼″
Total length, 4¾″
Length of hexagon end, 2″
Thickness of flange, ⅞″

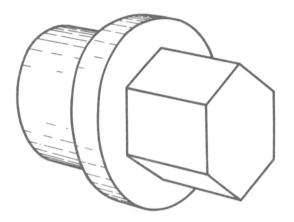

Problem 2 — Plug

Problem 3: Cylinder Head

Data:
Outside diameter, 5″
Small diameter, 3½″
Over-all thickness, 2¼″
Thickness at outer edge, 1½″
Counterbore, ¼″ deep x 4″
Diameter of drill circle, 4½″
Diameter of 6 holes, ¼″
FAO

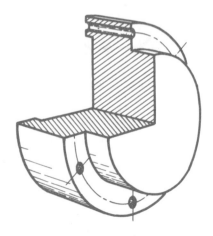

Problem 3 — Cylinder Head

Problem 4: Octagonal Riveting Hammer

Data:

Length, 4″
Width, 1″ x 1″
Radius at upper end, ⅛″
Opening for handle, ½″ x ¾″, located at center
    of length
Chamfers begin with end of hole for handle
Lower end of head, octagonal
FAO

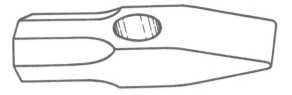

Problem 4 — Octagonal Riveting Hammer

Problem 5: End Support

Data:

Height, 4″
Top outside diameter, 3.375″
Octagonal base, 3.5″ across flats
Large hole, 2.25″ diameter x 2″ counterbore
Lower hole, 1.5″ diameter drilled through base
    and threaded 1½-12 UNF
Base, .625″ thick
Bevel inside, 30°
Fillet, .25″
Material, brass
FAO

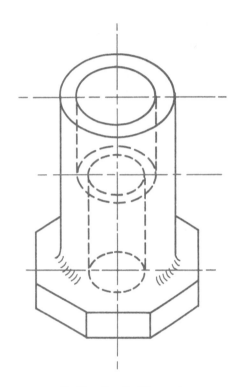

Problem 5 — End Support

40

Drawing Sectional Views

Some objects are constructed so the exact shape of the interior cannot clearly be shown with invisible-object lines; therefore a *sectional view* is required. This is a view of the interior that shows its exact shape in visible object lines. In making this view, imagine that part of the object has been removed, leaving the interior exposed. In order to make known to the workman that a view is in section, cross-hatching is used to contrast the surface where it is cut with the remainder of the drawing, as in Fig. 161.

There are several ways to show sectional views. When the entire front half of the object is supposed to have been removed, showing the whole view in section, Fig. 161, it is called a *full section*. When only half of the whole front is supposed to have been removed, showing half of the view in section, Fig. 162, it is called a *half section*.

Sometimes it is necessary to show the shape of a spoke, a rib, an arm, or other special part of an object. When this is necessary, a sectional view is made on the object at the desired place, as in Fig. 163. This is called a *revolved section*.

It may be necessary, in order to avoid confusion, not to make a revolved sectional view, but instead to make a *broken-out section,* as shown in Fig. 164. Then, too, there are times

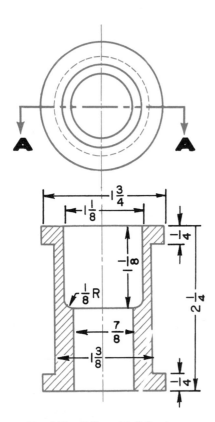

Fig. 161. Collar — Full Section

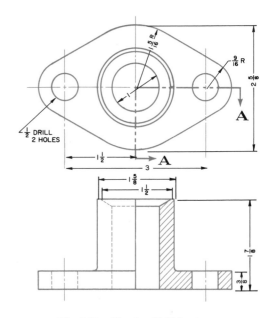

Fig. 162. Gland — Half Section

when only small parts or details require sectional views in order to make them clear. A small section removed from the view is drawn as in Fig. 165. This is called a *partial* or *detail section*.

1. If a full visible view with hidden-object lines will not give a clear idea of the construction of the object, make a sectional view. Choose the kind of sectional view that will show all that needs to be shown and no more.

2. Make the sectional view after all other views have been completed.

3. Draw a cutting-plane line across the surface to indicate the place where a sectional view is taken. On simple drawings where the location of the sectional view is clear, a cutting-plane line is not necessary. Figs. 161 and 162 are simple enough not to require cutting-plane lines. Fig. 23 in Unit 5 on conventional lines shows a cutting-plane line properly used.

4. Draw in the cross-hatching at 45° with fine lines spaced $\frac{1}{16}''$ apart. Space these lines uniformly and by eye. This can be done by starting the first spaces properly and watching the last one made while you space each new one.

5. When adjacent spaces are to be sectioned, draw the cross-hatching of the parts in opposite directions. Make the cross-hatching of the same part in the same direction. See Fig. 166.

6. When it is necessary to dimension in a cross-hatched area, place the dimension

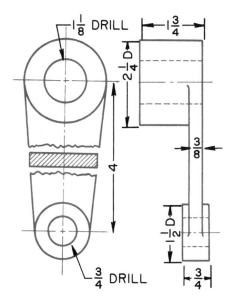

Fig. 164. Rocker Arm — Broken-Out Section

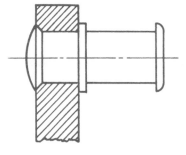

Fig. 165. Detail Section

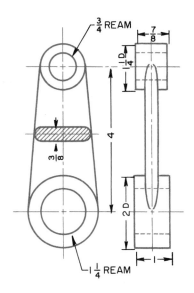

Fig. 163. Crank — Revolved Section

Fig. 166. Sectional View

figures first and then do the cross-hatching. Make it the practice to dimension the drawing before doing any of the cross-hatching.

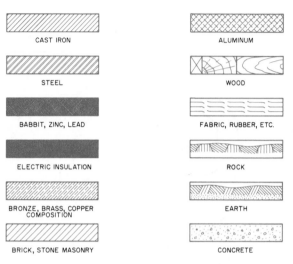

Fig. 167. Standard Material Symbols for Cross-Hatching

7. Invisible edges behind the sectional view need not be shown unless clarity demands it.

8. For most materials the cross-hatching shown in Figs. 161 to 165 is used and the name of the material is given. However, there are standard symbols for sectioning the many materials of industry. In Fig. 167 are shown several of the more common symbols.

Questions

1. The place where the sectional view is taken is indicated by a line consisting of heavy alternating long and two short dashes. This line is called a: (1) detail line, (2) section line, (3) construction line, (4) cutting-plane line (5) view line.

2. The main use of a sectional view is to indicate the material required in making the object. (True or False)

3. To what views in the top row in Fig. 168 do the sectional views in the bottom row belong?

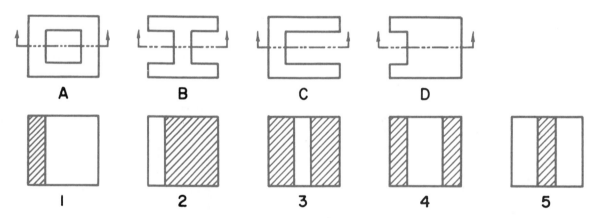

Fig. 168. Are These Sectional Drawings Correct?

PROBLEMS

Required: Working drawings of objects requiring sectional views.

Problem 1: Collar

Data:
Major outside diameter, 5¼″
Full thickness, 2¾″
Thickness of base, 1⅞″
Radius of fillet, 1⅛″
Diameter of hole, 1.25″
Counterbore, ³⁄₁₆″ x 1⅞″ dia.
Can be drawn with or without inside threads
See Fig. 172A for thread data for 1.25″ hole
Use UNC threads

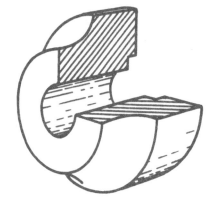

Problem 1 — Collar

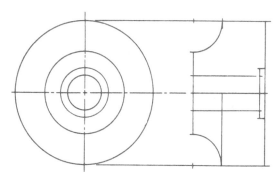

Step 1

Problem 2: Arbor Washer

Data:
Major outside diameter, 4″
Height, ¾″
Small diameter, 2⅜″
Diameter of hole, 1.25″
Counterbore, ⅛″ x 2¾″
Thickness of outer edge, ³⁄₁₆″

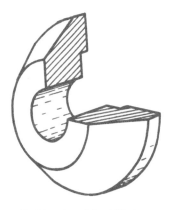

Problem 2 — Arbor Washer

129

Problem 3: Collar

Data:
Over-all length, 2⅛″
Diameter of flange, 4⅛″
Thickness of flange, ¹¹⁄₁₆″
Diameter of cylindrical projection, 1¼″
Diameter of hole, .75″
Can be drawn with or without threads, either UNC or UNF, any class fit.
FAO

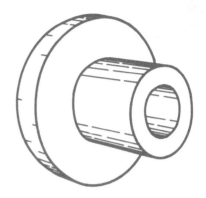

Problem 3 — Collar

Problem 4: Cylinder Head

Data:
Total length, 5¼″
Diameter of flange, 5½″
Thickness of flange, ¾″
Counterbore, ¼″ x 3½″
Diameter of cylindrical projection, 2½″
Diameter of shaft hole, 1.25″
Diameter of drill circle on flange, 4½″
Diameter of 6 holes, .5″
Material, cast iron
FAO

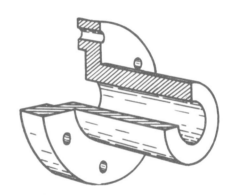

Problem 4 — Cylinder Head

Problem 5: Rocker Arm

Data:
Distance between centers of shaft holes in hubs, 8″
Diameter of hubs, 3″
Thickness, 1⅝″
Size of elliptical arm, 1″ x 2″
Projection of hubs above upper surface of arm, ⅛″
Runouts, ⅛″
Diameters of reamed holes, 2.000″ and 1.875″
(Flat surfaces of hubs finished 32)
Material, cast iron

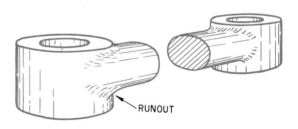

RUNOUT

Problem 5 — Rocker Arm

Problem 6: Compression Coupling

Data:

Outside diameter, 5.5″

Total length, 4.375″

Thickness of flange, .625″

Thickness of rim, .250″

Projection of rim each side of flange, .750″

Outside diameter of hub at large end, 2.750″; at small end, 2″

Length of hub, 3″

Diameter of hole at large end, 1.750″; taper per foot, 3″

Diameter of drill circle, 3.875″

Diameter of 6 drilled holes, .500″

Radius of fillets, .125″

FAO, finish 63

Material, steel

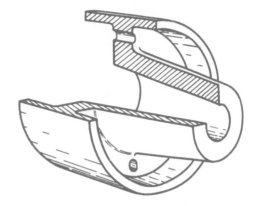

Problem 6 — Compression Coupling

Problem 7: Bronze Housing

Make a working drawing with necessary sectional view.

Data:

Dimension of base, .5″ x 2.5″ x 4″

Radii at corners, .5″

Outside of cylinder 1.5″, inside 1″, .625″ deep, with a .625″ hole through bottom

Height of cylinder, 2.25″

Total height, including base, 2.75″

Radius of fillet, .25″

Diameter of holes in base, .5″

Location of holes, 1.5″ from a center line perpendicular to the front, and .875″ from a center line perpendicular to the end

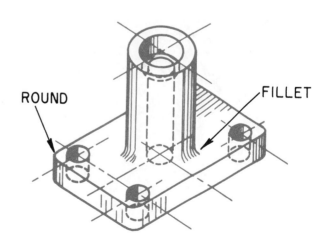

Problem 7 — Bronze Housing

Problem 8: End Bearing

   Data:

Total height, 7⅞″

Length of bearing, 3¼″

Base plate, 1″ x 5⅜″ x 8½″, with 1″ radius two
   corners

Back plate, ¾″ thick

Diameter of top hole, .75″, 2.5″ deep

Diameter of lower hole, 1.5″, 2.375″ deep

Diameter of holes in base plate, 1″

A = 1⅛″

B = 1½″

C = 1⅝″

D = 2⅞″

E = 1⅞″

F = Recess in bottom plate ½″ x 1″ x 3″,
     placed 1″ from front edge, symmetrical to
     center line

G = 2½″

H = 2¾″

J = 1¼″

K = 6″

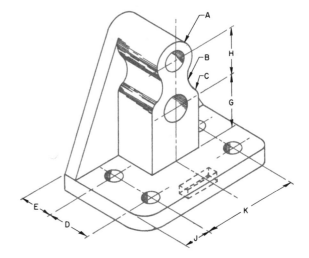

Problem 8 — End Bearing

Problem 9: Anchor Link

   Data:

A = 5.250″

B = 2″

C = .750″

D = .500″

E = ⅝″ drill

F = 1.5″ dia.

G = ½″ drill

H = .625″ radius

I = 1.250″

J = 1.500″

X is centered on Y

FAO

Material, steel

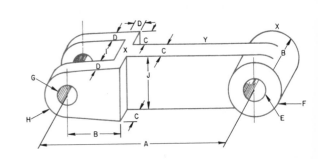

Problem 9 — Anchor Link

Problem 10: Rotor Bracket

Data:
A = 5¼″
B = 4½″
C = 3″
D = ⅝″
E = 1″
F = 1⅝″
G = 3¼″
H = .5625″ drill 3 holes
I = 1½″
J = ¾″ radius
FAO, finish 63
Material, steel

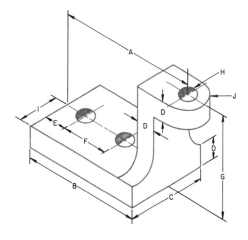

Problem 10 — Rotor Bracket

Problem 11: Support Arm

Data:
A = 2.75″
B = 3″
C = 1.5″
D = 1.625″
E = 2″ dia.
F = .75″ drill
G = .625″ radius
H = .5″ drill 2 holes (32 finish)
I = 1″
J = 1.25″
K = .75″
L = .25″
M = .25″ radius
N = .25″ drill to center
Machine surfaces (X) to FAO, finish 63
Material, cast aluminum

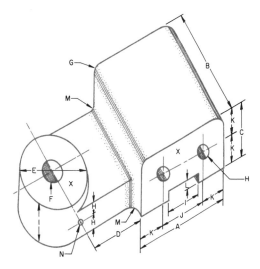

Problem 11 — Support Arm

Dividing a Straight Line into any Number of Equal Parts

It is often necessary in drafting to divide a line into a number of equal parts. Of course, some lines can be so divided with an ordinary scale. Distances difficult to measure may be divided accurately by construction with dividers and straightedge. The method here shown may be used in dividing the pitch of screw threads, in surface developments, and in similar situations involving this procedure.

1. Let the line *AB* represent any length line to be divided into equal parts. Take five equal parts, for example.

2. Draw line *AX* at any angle with line *AB*.

3. With the scale or dividers and beginning at *A*, lay off on *AX* five convenient equal divisions.

4. Connect points *X* and *B* with a straight line, Fig. 170.

5. Through points *1, 2, 3,* and *4* draw lines parallel to the line *XB* cutting the line *AB* into equal parts. See Unit 26.

Problem

Try to discover a way to locate points along the edge of a piece of leather 5 inches long that will be spaced in the same relative distances as *1, 2,* and *3*.

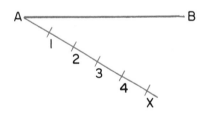

Fig. 169. Dividing a Line, First Step

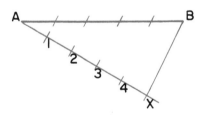

Fig. 170. Dividing a Line, Second Step

Screw Threads

Machine Screws and Bolts Used in Manufacture

The most common fastenings for machine parts are bolts and screws. Bolts and screws make the assembly of machines a rather simple task. Because of the threads, it is possible to hold the parts firmly in position, and yet the threads also make it possible to readily take the machine apart for repairs or replacements.

In Fig. 171, a few of the most common bolts and screws are shown. In Fig. 172, the common screw threads are shown. Bolts and screws are made by cutting threads on rods. These may be of different lengths and sizes, and with different shapes of heads. It is necessary, in order to assemble machines, to drill holes and thread them on the inside so that a bolt or screw can

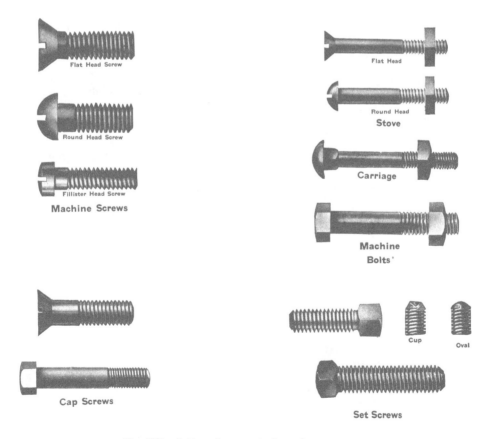

Fig. 171. A Few Common Bolts and Screws

be turned into them. The threads on the outside of bolts and screws are called *external threads*. Those on the inside of holes are called *internal threads*.

Machine screws are used to fasten two metal parts together. One part has a drilled hole through which the screw is passed and screwed into a threaded hole in the second. Machine screws have either round, flat, oval, oval fillister, or flat fillister slotted heads.

Cap screws are used for fastening one metal part to another by passing it through a hole in one piece and screwing it into a tapped hole.

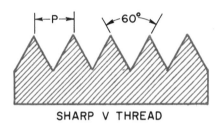

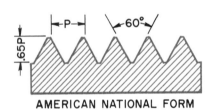

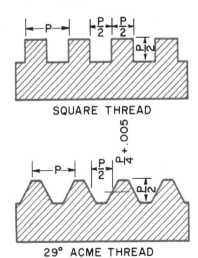

Fig. 172. Common Thread Forms

Wrench head hexagon; slotted flat, button and oval fillister, and socket heads are available. *Stove bolts* are used to hold two or more metal parts together by passing the bolts through holes in each part and fastening with square nuts.

Carriage bolts are used to hold two or more parts together by passing the bolts through holes in two or more parts and fastening with a square nut. One or more parts may be metal. A squared portion under the head, equal to the diameter of the bolt, is designed to prevent the bolt from turning in the wooden part. Washers are often used under the nut to secure a tight joint and prevent cutting a wooden part.

Machine bolts are used to hold two metal parts together by passing them through holes in each part and fastening with a nut. Washers under the nut are often used to secure the tightness of a joint.

Set screws are used for holding collars, pulleys, and other machine parts in place. They are made either with square wrench heads or are slotted or socket headless. Set screws may have oval, cone, flat, or dog points.

Sizes of Screws

The size of a screw is indicated by the diameter and the number of threads per inch. The size of screw threads is indicated by fractions or by screw gage numbers. Thread sizes of ¼″ and larger are designated by fractions, such as ¼—20 National Coarse, ¼—28 Unified National Coarse, and ¼—36 Extra Fine on Table III. Screw diameters of less than ¼″ are designated by screw gage numbers, such as No. 10 diameter for the diameter of 0.190″ on Table III.

The series in common use are the American National Coarse and the American National Fine. The American National Series with slight modifications which has become the standard for Canada and Great Britain is called the Unified Thread Series. The main difference between the American National Series and the Unified Series is the shape of the root and crest. The root in the Unified Series is usually rounded by the cutting tool, and the crest may be flat or rounded, Fig. 172.

Classes of Fit

The United States of America Standards Institute (USAS), formerly the American Standards

Association (ASA), classifies threads according to the accuracy necessary in the manufacture of an object. Some objects which require precision fitting are (1) measuring, drafting, and scientific instruments, (2) special gages, and (3) automotive and aircraft parts that must absorb vibrations under great stress; therefore, very fine threads must be used in assembly. Objects of less accuracy for quick assembly, such as stove bolts, do not require precision-cut threads.

Threads, therefore, are cut with different degrees of accuracy. These are indicated by *classes of fit*. There are four classes: loose fit or *class 1*, free fit or *class 2*, medium fit or *class 3*, close fit or *class 4*.

Class 4 (close fit) is not often used in mass production, but when hand assembly is necessary, such as in fine instruments, it is required.

Class 2 (free fit) threads are accurately made and used in mass production assembly work where interchangeable screw threads are desired in production. If parts are to be assembled and movement of parts is not a problem as in fastening permanent fixtures, class 1 (loose fit) threads may be used.

Drawing the Threads

The true thread form is difficult to draw and it is unnecessary for practical purposes. A much quicker method is to draw conventional representations as shown in Fig. 173. This form is so widely used that it is as well understood by the workman as is the drawing of the true thread form. Observe that there is a convention for internal threads in a sectional view as well as for the external threads and they are alike.

In a working drawing that shows threads, it is necessary to use symbols to give the workman all the data needed, so a note is lettered near the

Table III
SCREW THREADS

No.	DIAMETER INCH	DIAMETER DECIMAL EQUIVALENT	UNC (NC) (USS)	UNF (NF) (SAE)	EF (EXTRA FINE)
0	...	.0600	...	80	...
1	...	.0730	64	72	...
2	...	.0860	56	64	...
3	...	.0990	48	56	...
4	...	.1120	40	48	...
5	1/8	.1250	40	44	...
6	...	.1380	32	40	...
8	...	.1640	32	36	...
10	...	.1900	24	32	40
12	...	.2160	24	28	...
...	1/4	.2500	20	28	36
...	5/16	.3125	18	24	32
...	3/8	.3750	16	24	32
...	7/16	.4375	14	20	28
...	1/2	.5000	13	20	28
...	9/16	.5625	12	18	24
...	5/8	.6250	11	18	24
...	3/4	.7500	10	16	20
...	7/8	.8750	9	14	20
...	1	1.0000	8	14	20

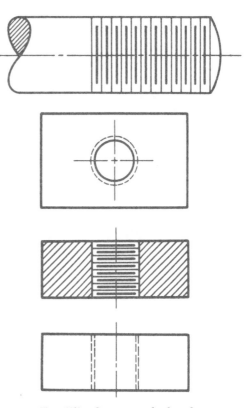

Fig. 173. Conventional Threads

thread. For example: ⅝-11 UNC-2 means that the bolt is ⅝″ in diameter, there are to be 11 threads per inch, the Unified National Coarse thread form is to be used, and a class 2 fit is required. Most threads are tightened by turning to the right and need not be indicated, but a left-hand thread must be marked *LH* as in E of Fig. 174. Tables covering the necessary data are obtained by draftsmen from the various draftsmen's handbooks.

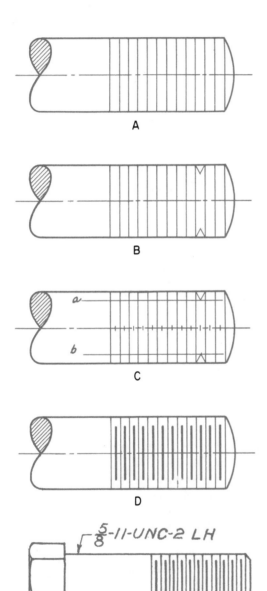

A

B

C

D

⅝-11-UNC-2 LH

E

Fig. 174. Procedure for Drawing Conventional Screw Threads

To represent American National standard screw threads conventionally proceed as follows:

1. Determine the diameter and the pitch of the threads to be drawn.

2. Lay off the spaces for the threads. For example: if a 1″ bolt with 8 threads per inch is to be drawn, lay off the spaces equal to the pitch, ⅛″.

3. Draw light lines across the bolt to represent the outside points or the *crest* for each thread as shown in A of Fig. 174.

4. American National standard threads are cut at 60°.

5. Draw intersecting 60° lines on opposite sides as shown in B of Fig. 174.

6. Through the points of intersection, draw construction lines *a* and *b* to mark the depth of the threads.

7. On the center line, locate the midpoints representing the *roots* of the threads, as in C of Fig. 174.

8. Draw heavy lines through these points from line *a* to line *b*.

9. In Fig. 174 is shown the completed conventional external thread in regular form.

10. Internal threads would be drawn in a similar way.

11. The plan view of internal threads, or the view as seen when you look into the hole, is represented by two circles as shown in

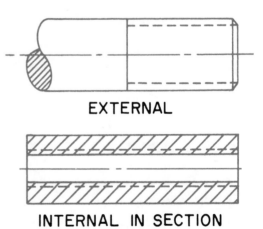

EXTERNAL

INTERNAL IN SECTION

Fig. 175A. Simplified Thread Symbols

Fig. 173. The solid line represents the crests and the hidden line represents the roots of the internal threads.

12. Simplified symbols for external and for internal threads in section are shown in Fig. 175A. The broken lines indicate the root line. The semi-conventional symbols show the shape of the thread and the crest and root lines, Fig. 175B.

Problem

1. Draw a threaded rod showing conventional screw threads. The rod is 6″ long and 1″ in diameter. It is threaded 2″ on each end with National Coarse threads. A Class 2 fit is to be used. The table of National Coarse screw thread sizes would show that there should be 8 threads per inch. Letter a note near the threads as follows: 1–8 UNC-2.

Questions

1. Explain why screws are better for fastening most machine parts than are rivets.

2. Explain why a machine part becomes fixed firmly when the screw is turned one way and is loosened when the screw is turned the other way. Use a screw to show what action takes place.

3. Why not draw the true shapes of the threads in a working drawing?

4. When drawing conventional threads the lines representing the threads should be evenly spaced. Should the heavy lines representing the roots be the same length?

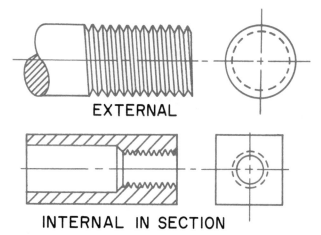

EXTERNAL

INTERNAL IN SECTION

Fig. 175B. Semi-Conventional Thread Symbols

Unit 43

Standardization of Parts and Tools

In the manufacturing industries it has been found desirable to standardize certain parts used in construction. Among the many items used are bolts, screws, keys, rivets, springs, machine parts, pipe and pipe fittings, gears, cams, small tools and machine tool elements; also used are the symbols and abbreviations for drafting room practice which complete the graphic language necessary to convey information to workmen. Assembly of units and parts of automobiles such as oil pumps, piston rings, and distributor arms are examples of many items that have been standardized.

The United States of America Standards Institute works continually on standardization of parts and tools. The foregoing list is merely suggestive of the large number of standardized items. A com-

plete and current listing may be obtained by writing the USAS office.[1]

Maintenance efficiency as well as economy and convenience of manufacture are made possible by standardizing parts. Without this very important service, manufacture would be more costly than it is. A designer in the drafting room should use standard parts wherever possible. An especially designed part increases the cost of manufacture.

Questions

1. What is meant by standardization?
2. What is the advantage of having uniformity of parts and of tools in a garage?
3. Give examples of parts or tools other than those listed that you believe are standardized. You may use a reference such as the USAS list.

[1]United States of America Standards Institute, 345 East 47th St., New York, N.Y.

Drawing a Simple Auxiliary View

You have learned to make a working drawing in which one, two, or three views have been enough to give the necessary information for construction. Sometimes even the three common views of a working drawing, the front, side, and top, will not give enough information. Because of the shape of the object, it will be necessary to draw a helping or auxiliary view.

The three common views show true shapes because each is taken exactly parallel with a surface, but when there is another surface that can-

not be shown in true shape with regular views, as A in Fig. 176, the auxiliary view must be made. This view also must be taken parallel with the surface. The procedure used in making an auxiliary view of Fig. 176 will serve in making such views of other objects that require it.

1. On the view that gives the true width of the object, place numbers at each corner of the top view. The top view in Fig. 176 shows this width and the numbers *1, 2, 3, 4, 5,* and

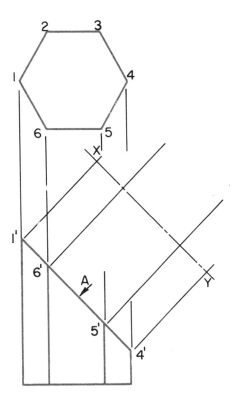

Fig. 176. Drawing Auxiliary View, First Step

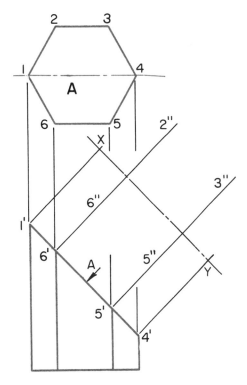

Fig. 177. Drawing Auxiliary View, Second Step

6 are properly placed. Label *1′* ("one prime"), *6′, 5′,* and *4′* on surface A to correspond.

2. Draw a center line *XY* at right angles to these lines and parallel with line *1′ ′4*. Place this center line far enough away from the object to allow space for the auxiliary view.

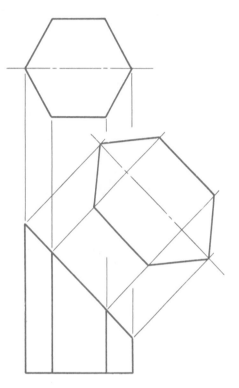

Fig. 178. Drawing Auxiliary View, Third Step

3. Draw construction lines from points *1′, 6′, 5′,* and *4′* perpendicular to line *1′ 4′,* the edge view of surface A, Fig. 176.

4. Draw a center line through points *1* and *4* of top view, Fig. 177. Set one leg of the dividers on point *2* of the top view and take off the distance to the center line. Transfer this distance by placing one leg of the dividers on center line *XY* at a point where the construction line perpendicular to *6′* crosses it, then mark the necessary distances at *6″* and *2″* with the other leg of the dividers.

5. Since distance *2-6* in the top view is equal to distance *3-5,* the same setting of the dividers as in step *4* is used in laying off distances *5″-3″* in the auxiliary view.

6 Connect points *X, 2″, 3″, Y, 5″* and *6″* with straight lines and you will have the auxiliary view showing the true shape of surface A. See Fig. 178.

7. If your auxiliary view is correct, the opposite sides will be equal and parallel.

Questions

1. How can you determine, by measuring one of the views in Fig. 176 the right distance away from line *1′ 4′* to place center line *XY?*

2. Why must the center line *XY* be parallel to surface *A?*

3. Why does the width of the auxiliary view correspond to the length of surface *A.*

Drawing an Ellipse

If you were to cut a cylinder or a cone at an angle, the shape of the surface of the cut portion would be an ellipse. If you turn the end of a round rod or round stick away from you at an angle so you will not be looking directly at it, you will see the circle change in shape to an ellipse. There is a mathematical formula for the ellipse, but it can be drawn without knowing the formula.

There are many methods of drawing an ellipse. Some are more accurate than others. You will be shown one accurate method and three other methods that give approximately correct results.

Concentric Circle Method — Accurate

1. Let *AB* be the major axis and *CD* be the minor axis, Fig. 179.

2. Draw two circles on the same center, one with its diameter equal to *AB* and the other equal to *CD*.

3. Divide the circles into an equal number of parts and draw radial lines. Line *1-2* is one such line. There are 12 equal parts in Fig. 179, but 24 would be more accurate.

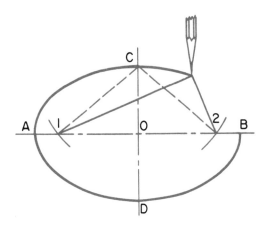

Fig. 180. Drawing Ellipse, Pin and String Method

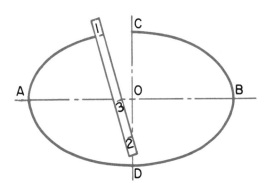

Fig. 181. Drawing Ellipse, Trammel Method

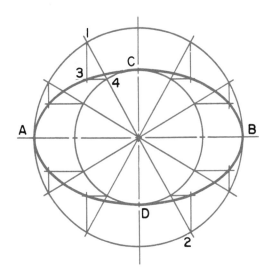

Fig. 179. Drawing Ellipse, Concentric Circle Method

4. Draw vertical lines toward the inner circle from the points were the radial lines cut the outer circle, as *1-3.*

5. Draw horizontal lines toward the outer circle from the points where the radial lines cut the inner circle, as *3-4.*

6. The intersection of *1-3* and *3-4* and all other such intersections are the points through which the ellipse is drawn.

7. Continue with steps *5* and *6* until all points of the ellipse are located.

8. Draw free-hand an even curve through each point thus located, and smooth it with the irregular curve as a guide.

Pin and String Method (For Large Elipses)

1. Let *AB* be the major axis and *CD* be the minor axis. Fig. 180.

2. With *AO* as a radius and *C* as a center, draw arcs intersecting line *AB* at points *1* and *2.* Points *1* and *2* are called the *foci* (fosi).

3. Press pins securely into the board at points *1, 2,* and *C.*

4. Fasten a string to pin number *1,* pull it snugly around pin *C* and fasten the end to pin *2.*

5. Remove pin *C,* and replace it with a pencil. With light, steady, outward pressure move the pencil inside the string to draw the ellipse.

Trammel Method

1. Let *AB* and *CD* be the major and minor axes, Fig. 181.

2. On the straight edge of a piece of stiff paper or a card, lay off distance *1-2* equal to *AO* and distance *1-3* equal to *CO.* This will be your trammel.

3. With point *3* kept on the major axis and point *2* on the minor axis, locate at point *1* a point on the curve. Mark this point.

4. Continue to move the trammel and at point *1* on the straightedge locate points on the curve at several positions until the ellipse is laid out. Draw a line through these points to complete the ellipse.

Compasses Method — Approximate

The following is a quick, approximate method of drawing an ellipse or a circle in isometric form. Templates are available, Fig. 182A. In the absence of a template or if you wish to draw an ellipse which is too large for an available template, the following method may be used (Fig. 182B):

1. Assume that a 2″ circle is to be drawn in isometric form. Draw a circle, *1,2,3,4,* as at *X,* Fig. 182B.

2. Draw the 2″ square, *A,B,C,D,* with the sides tangent to the circle at points *1,2,3,4.*

3. Draw the isometric square as in *Y,* Fig. 182B.

4. At the points *1,2,3,4,* with the 30-60 triangle, draw lines perpendicular to the sides. Lines *1-C* and *4-C* will intersect and form the center for arc *4-1.* The point of intersection of lines *3-A* and *2-A* will form the center for arc *3-2.*

5. Intersection of lines *A-2* and *C-1* will form the center for arc *1-2.* Lines *C-4* and *A-3* will intersect to form the center for arc *3-4.* The four arcs will compose the desired ellipse.

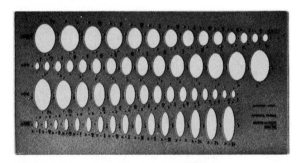

Fig.182A. Templates are Available in Many Geometrical Forms (Courtesy, The Lietz Company)
They are used as a time-saving device for draftsmen.

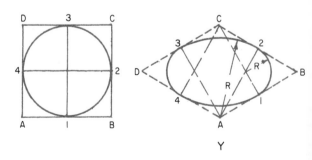

Fig. 182B. Drawing an Ellipse (Approximate Method)

PROBLEMS

Required: Working drawings of objects that involve auxiliary views.

Problem 1: Truncated (Cut) Hexagonal Pyramid

Data:
Length of each side of base, 1″
Apex height of pyramid, 3½″
Height above the base of uppermost point of the truncated surface, 2¼″
Angle of truncated surface to the base, 45°

Problem 2: Truncated Cylinder

Data:
Diameter, 1¾″
Total height, 3″
Height on extreme right, ¾″

Problem 3: Bracket

Data:
Angle formed by bracket, 120°
Thickness of material, ⅜″
Width of bracket, 2″
Height of vertical part, 1¾″
Slant height of slotted part, 2″
Drilled holes,
    ⅜″ diameter,
    centered 1″
    apart, ½″
    from edge
Slot ⅜″ wide; full length, 1¼″,
    centered in slanting part

Problem 1
Truncated Hexagonal
Pyramid

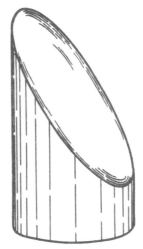

Problem 2 —
Truncated Cylinder

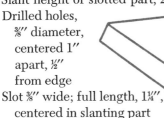
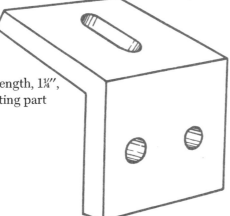

Problem 3 — Bracket

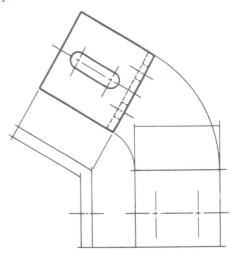

Step 1

Problem 4: Angle Stop

Data:

Width of piece, 2.25″

Thickness of material, .5″

Height of vertical part, 2.5″

Slant height of upper part, 2.5″

Angle of opening, 120°

2 drilled holes, .375″ diameter, centered .875″
  apart; lower one centered .625″ from bottom
  (holes can be tapped 16-NC-2)

Diameter of reamed hole centered in oblique
  slant surface, 1″

Keyway for .25″ square key

Corner radius, .375″

FAO

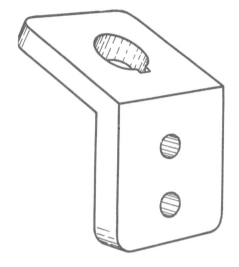

Problem 4 — Angle Stop

Problem 5: Adjusting Bracket

Data:

Change to decimals before drawing

Diameter of ring, 3½″

Thickness of ring, ⅝″

Diameter of hole, 2.25″

Thickness of lug, 5/16″

Width of lug, 1½″

Angle of lug, 45° to axis of ring

Upper edge of bend in lug, 1¾″ from center of
  ring

Slant length of lug, 3″

Length of slot, 1¾″

Width of slot, .500″

Center of lower end of slot concentric with
  lower end of lug

FAO

Problem 5 — Adjusting Bracket

Problem 6: Support

Data:

Thickness of base, ¾″

Width of base, 2″

Length of base, 4″

Base cut away to ⅜″ thick, 1″ from end

Slant surface, 1½″ wide, 3″ long

Angle of slant surface, 30° to horizontal

Reamed hole, ⅝″ dia., concentric with upper
  end of slant surface

FAO, finish 63

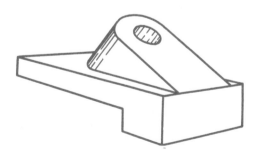

Problem 6 — Support

Problem 7: Fixed Clip

Data:

Change to decimals before drawing

Base, 6″ x 6½″ x 1″

Holes in base, 1″ dia., centered 2″ from front, 1½″ from right side, 3″ apart

Back, 1″ thick, 5½″ high, set at 30°

Holes in back, .75″ dia., centered 4¼″ from base

A = 1″ radius

B = 1¼″ radius

FAO, finish 63

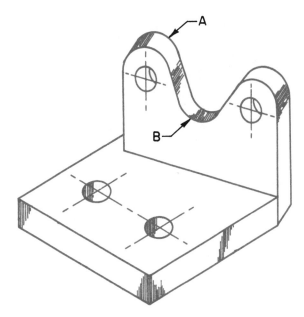

Problem 7 — Fixed Clip

Problem 8: Adjustable Clip

Data:

Center section, ¾″ x 3½″ x 4½″

Four holes, ½″ diameter, ⅞″ from edge, 1¾″ on centers 1″ from clip

Lower connector, ¾″ x 3″ x 3½″, 15° from *H*

Slot, ½″ x 1¼″, center to center, 1″ from end

Radius each corner, ⅜″

Upper clip, ¾″ x 3″ x 3½″, 30° from *H*

End slot, 1″ x ⅞″ on center from end

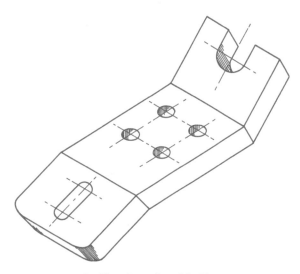

Problem 8 — Adjustable Clip

Problem 9: Hex Clip

Data:
Width, 3″
Length of A, 2¾″
Angle between *A* and *B*, 30°
Dimension *B* is 2⁹⁄₁₆″
Lower end, ⅝″ radius
Thickness, ⅝″
Rounds, ⅝″ radius
Concave curve, ⅝″
2 holes, .625″ diameter, 1⅝″ apart on center
   line which is 1⁵⁄₁₆″ from top
Hole *C*, .375″ diameter, 1¼″ from center line of
   2 holes
Hexagonal opening, 1″ across flats and cen-
   tered
FAO, finish 63

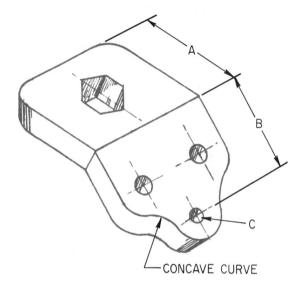

Problem 9 — Hex Clip

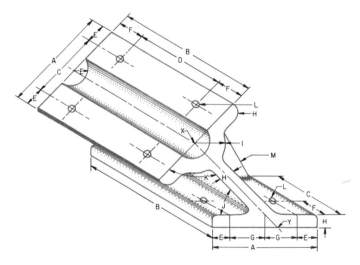

Problem 10 — Bearing Bracket

Problem 10: Bearing Bracket

Data:
A = 3″
B = 4″
C = 2″
D = 2.5″
E = .5″
F = .75″
G = 1″
H = .375″ radius and thickness
I = .875″ radius
J = 45°
K = 90°
L = .125″ drilled holes
M = brace .375″ thick centered on base at 60°
    starting .25″ from edge
Distance X″ to Y″ = 3.375″
Material, bronze
FAO, finish 32

Making an Assembly Drawing

A drawing that shows an object as it would appear when constructed with all its parts in place is called an *assembly drawing.* Fig. 183 shows the relative positions of all the parts of the object. Important dimensions often are given and partial sections and even half sections are shown.

Assembly drawings are of several kinds and are used in many types of work in which working drawings are required. One form of assembly drawing is used in planning the general structure of an object, after which the working drawings of the various parts are made. Another form of assembly drawing is used as a guide for assembling the parts of an object. Such a drawing is usually made from the working drawings of the parts, and general dimensions are given for the workman to follow in checking the placement of the parts.

A third form of assembly drawing is used in connection with selling or with directions for operating a machine. Such drawings are found in catalogs and in handbooks of instruction. It can be said also that pipe and wiring diagrams, heating, steel and stone plans are forms of assembly drawings.

The making of a designer's assembly drawing is very advanced work and it requires such abilities as are possessed by engineers or inventors or special designers. The making of a construction assembly drawing is most often the work of a draftsman. If one can make correctly the drawings of the parts, it is rather simple to make the assembly.

1. Examine the drawings of the parts, *detail drawings,* and determine which is the body or the main part.

2. Take notes on the general dimensions covering center-to-center distances from part-

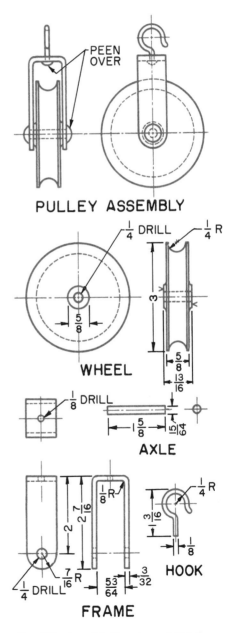

Fig. 183. Assembly Drawing and Details

to-part and over-all distances of the various parts.

3. Assembly drawings are usually made to smaller scale than are the detail drawings because all the parts assembled may make a very large structure. You can determine the necessary scale after you have made the sketch.

4. On sketching paper, first sketch the center lines for the main part and then the center lines for the remaining parts.

5. Sketch the main part and then add the detail parts, making related round and symmetrical portions around the center lines first and straight lines and small details later.

6. Place any general dimensions or notes that would be necessary for the workman to follow.

7. Check the sketch of the assembly with the details to see that it is complete.

8. Decide on the necessary scale to which the assembly must be drawn.

9. Make the mechanical drawing of the assembly by following the sketch, locating main center lines first, then making circles and symmetrical parts that are related to each other, and finally drawing the details and placing general dimensions and notes. The making of the mechanical drawing of the assembly is the copying with instruments of all that was sketched.

10. Check the assembly drawing to see that it is complete.

11. Hidden edges are usually not shown in assembly drawings except when principal ones are necessary for the workman.

12. Sectional views are shown only when the workman must have them to do his job correctly.

Questions

1. The diagram for a door bell circuit is one form of assembly drawing. (True or False)

2. A two-view working drawing of a carpenter's horse with all its parts nailed in place would be an assembly drawing. (True or False)

3. Why place all center lines first in making an assembly drawing?

Drawing to Scale

You have previously learned that when an object is too large to be drawn its full size, it is necessary to draw it smaller and to proportion. For example, to draw to full size the plans for a house, a cupboard, a car, or a map for a city, would require a piece of paper much too large to draw upon. When an object is very small, it is drawn larger than full size scale.

Architect's and engineer's scales are made for drawing to scale and they are marked so there is little difficulty in making drawings smaller or larger than full size. The dimension numbers give the actual size measurements of the object. The numbers never change, regardless of the scale to which the drawing is made.

1. Next to full size, the most common reduction is *half-size* scale of 6″ = 1′-0″, six inches being one-half of a foot. Six inches on the full-size scale represent one foot, and a half inch represents one inch. You need only imagine that a half inch is an inch and proceed to draw.

2. The next reduction possible is to quarter-size scale, 3″ = 1′-0″, three inches being one-quarter of a foot. Locate the end of an architect's scale that has the large figure 3 marked on it. Three full inches are divided into small graduations to represent a one-foot scale. There are twelve divisions to represent twelve inches. Each of the twelve divisions is divided into fractional parts of an inch. In making a drawing to the scale 3″ = 1′-0″ you would make all measurements with this quarter-size scale.

3. If quarter-size scale is too large, one-eighth-size may be used. On the other end of the scale from that marked with the figure 3 is a space marked 1½. It represents one foot and is written, Scale 1½″ = 1′-0″. This is marked

into twelve divisions to represent twelve inches. If you wish to draw to one-eighth scale you need only assume that the graduated 1½ inch is a foot and proceed to make measurements as usual.

4. In drawing house plans a quarter inch is used to represent one foot, ¼″ = 1′-0″. If the plans would be very large, as for a large building, an eighth inch is used to represent a foot. It is expressed, Scale: ⅛″ = 1′-0″.

5. Details for house plans, such as special drawings for cupboards, fireplaces, window and door frames, are drawn to a larger scale than are the floor plans. Various reductions are used but 1½″ = 1′-0″ and ¾″ = 1′-0″ are common. Builders like the scale 1½″ = 1′-0″ for special details because measurements can be checked readily with the common pocket rule.

6. Maps must be drawn to a much smaller scale than are house plans and machine parts. Maps are made with the engineer's scale which is marked into decimal graduations. The reductions of maps vary, depending upon the size of the area to be mapped. A common scale for a map of a small area is 1″ = 100′ and a common scale for a map of a large area is 1″ = 5000′.

Questions

1. Why not use 4″ = 1′-0″ as a scale? Or 2″ = 1′-0″?

2. Draw three straight lines, 4″, 1″ and 2″ respectively. If each line represents 8″ what is the scale for each?

3. Draw top and end views of a vise jaw. The vise jaw is ½″ x 4″ x 7″. Draw to ½ scale.

PROBLEMS

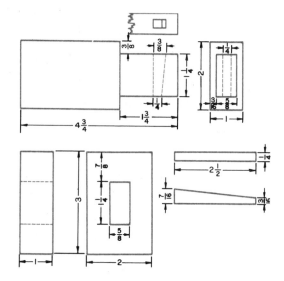

Required: To make an assembly drawing from details.

Problem 1: Details of Keyed Mortise and Tenon Joint

Problem 1 — Details of Keyed Mortise and Tenon Joint

Problem 2: Mechanics Clamp

From the details of the mechanics clamp at the right, make an assembly drawing.

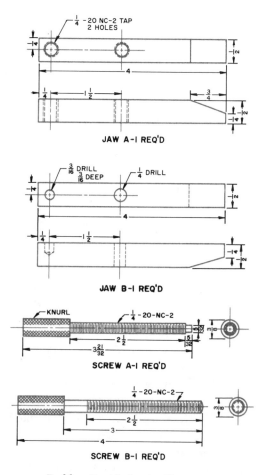

Problem 2 — Mechanics Clamp

Problem 3: Toolmaker's Vise

Make assembly drawing from the details of the toolmaker's vise. The material is steel. Identify the parts by number on the assembly drawing.

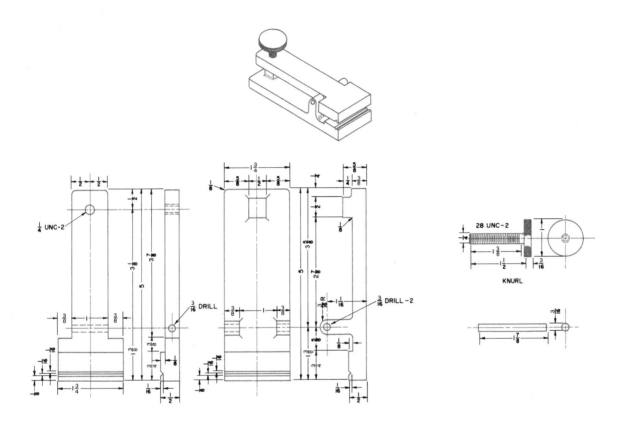

Problem 3 — Toolmaker's Vise

Problem 4:

From the shop or the drafting room, select an object of several parts — one that requires detail and assembly drawings. Make the working sketches, have them approved and then make the completed drawings.

Drawings that show objects somewhat as they would appear in a photograph are called pictorial drawings. The most common of these are known as *perspective, oblique, and isometric drawings.*

Perspective drawings, Fig. 184, more nearly represent an object as it really appears to the eye than do oblique and isometric drawings. In a perspective drawing the parallel lines that recede from the eye converge or seem to come together as do railroad tracks in the distance. Because oblique and pictorial drawings are somewhat easier to make, they are often used instead of perspective drawings.

The receding lines in *oblique drawings* do not converge but remain parallel with each other. In oblique drawings, the face of the object is shown in true form. The vertical lines are really vertical. The lines that recede from the eye may be drawn at any angle, but the most common angles are 30°, 60°, and 45°, Figs. 185, 186, and 187.

When the receding lines are drawn at an angle and in their full length, the drawing is called a *cavalier drawing.* When the receding lines are drawn at 45° and at half their true length, the drawing is called a *cabinet drawing.* To give a thicker effect, the receding lines sometimes are made two-thirds or three-fourths the full size. In perspective, the foreshortening of the receding lines is approximated. Cabinet drawing is so

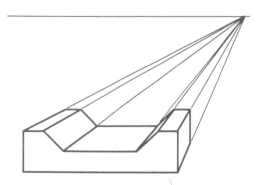

Fig. 184. Perspective. The Lines Seem to Come Together in the Distance

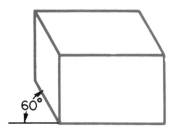

Fig. 186. Sixty Degree Oblique Drawing

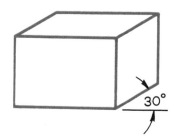

Fig. 185. Thirty Degree Oblique Drawing

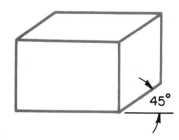

Fig. 187. Forty-Five Degree Oblique Drawing

named because it is often used to make drawings of cabinet work.

Isometric drawings seem more nearly like perspective. Horizontal lines recede 30° to the right and 30° to the left and may be drawn to less than full size, thus resembling perspective. However, unlike perspective, the receding lines are parallel.

In isometric drawing, Fig. 188, three faces of an object are shown, the top and two sides. There are three axes, a vertical line, a line at 30° to the right and a line at 30° to the left from the vertical axis. These three lines are 120° apart and form a set of isometric lines. When isometric lines are used as axes from which measurements are made, they are called *isometric coordinate axes*. Vertical lines on the object appear vertical in the drawing. Horizontal lines forming right angles on the object are drawn at 30° to the horizontal.

Because of the regularity of the receding lines and their full–scale length, an isometric drawing seems out of shape and too large. The apparent oversize may be overcome by drawing the thirty degree lines to isometric scale. An isometric scale is obtained by transferring the divisions of a standard scale to a forty-five degree line, and then projecting them to a thirty degree line as in Fig. 189.

Making a Cabinet Drawing

1. Draw the front face of the object, making the horizontal lines of the object horizontal and the vertical lines vertical. See Fig. 190, *a, b, c, d.*
2. From three corners, *a, b,* and *c,* of the front view draw the receding lines at 45°. In Fig. 190, a line has been drawn to the right from each of the upper corners and one line from the lower corner. Make the lines to scale one-half the true length of the receding lines of the object.
3. To complete the drawing connect the ends of the receding lines, Fig. 191. The finished drawing shows the front, top, and right end faces.

   If the receding lines are drawn to the left, the left end is shown as in Fig. 192. Similarly, if the receding lines are drawn downward to the right or to the left, the bottom face of the object is shown with either the right or the left face, Fig. 193.

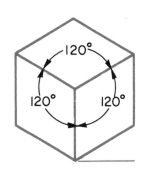

Fig. 188. Isometric Drawing

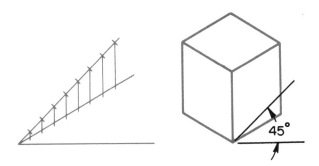

Fig. 189. Obtaining Isometric Scale

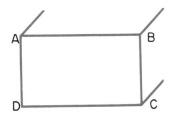

Fig. 190. Cabinet Drawing, First Step

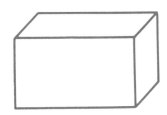

Fig. 191. Cabinet Drawing Showing Right End

Fig. 192. Cabinet Drawing Showing Left End

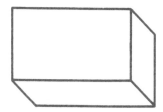

Fig. 193. Cabinet Drawing Showing Bottom End

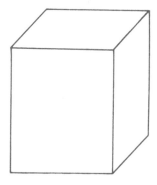

Fig. 194. Making a Cabinet Drawing of an Irregular Shape, First Step

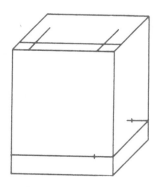

Fig. 195. Making a Cabinet Drawing of an Irregular Shape, Second Step

Making a Cabinet Drawing of Irregular Shape

Irregular shapes may easily be drawn using horizontal, vertical, and 45 degree lines as axes from which to measure much the same as from the working face, the working edge, and the end of a squared piece of stock. In any drawing the draftsman will be greatly aided if he will visualize the steps required in making the object which he is drawing. Remember that the drawing is to tell the workman how the object is to be made.

1. In making a cabinet drawing of irregular shape, first draw an enclosing rectangular solid, Fig. 194.
2. Measure off on basic lines any required distances, and draw corresponding horizontal, vertical, and 45 degree lines as shown in Fig. 195.
3. Connect the points thus located as in Fig. 196.

Making an Isometric Drawing

1. Draw the vertical axis *ab*, Fig. 197, the full height of the object, or it can be drawn to scale.
2. Draw the axes from *a* with one line 30° on the right and one line 30° on the left. Fig. 197.
3. On these axes measure off the length and the width of the object full size or to scale, locating the points *c* and *d* as in Fig. 197.
4. Draw the 30° axis *be* and *bf*, Fig. 198, from the bottom of the vertical axis.

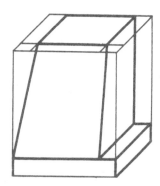

Fig. 196. Making a Cabinet Drawing of an Irregular Shape, Third Step

5. Draw the vertical lines through *c* and *d*, Fig. 199.

6. Complete the upper face by drawing *dg* and *cg* at 30°, Fig. 200.

Making a Perspective Drawing

It is rather difficult to make a perspective drawing without a great deal of practice. However, for ordinary use of the draftsman, the ability to apply some of the more common principles of perspective will be all that is necessary. With a little practice, fairly correct and neat perspective sketches can be made. A few of the more important principles involved are:

a. *Vertical lines of an object appear vertical in the sketch, Fig. 201.*

b. *Horizontal lines extending away from the eye appear to converge in a point on a level with the eye in the horizon. In the picture the horizon is represented by a horizontal line, Fig. 201.*

c. *Horizontal lines that are perpendicular to the horizon vanish in the center of vision, C. V., a point exactly opposite the eye, Fig. 201.*

d. *Horizontal lines parallel to the horizon are sketched parallel to the horizon line, Fig. 201.*

When the horizontal lines are parallel to the horizon or converge in the center of vision, the sketch is called a parallel perspective.

e. *Horizontal lines extending away from the eye and neither parallel nor perpendicular to the horizon converge in vanishing points on the*

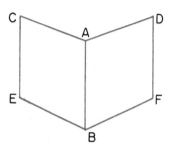

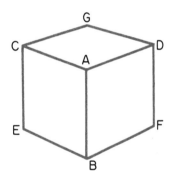

Fig. 199. Making an Isometric Drawing, Third Step

Fig. 200. Making an Isometric Drawing, Fourth Step

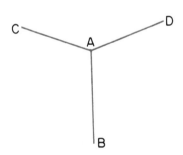

Fig. 197. Making an Isometric Drawing, First Step

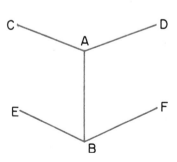

Fig. 198. Making an Isometric Drawing, Second Step

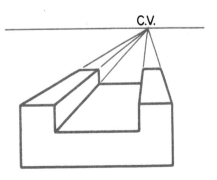

Fig. 201. Parallel Perspective

horizon line on either side of the center of vision. Horizontal lines extending to the right converge in a vanishing point at the right; those extending to the left converge in a vanishing point at the left.

When one series of the receding lines of a drawing appear to vanish to the right and another to the left, the sketch is called an angular perspective, Fig. 202.

f. *The direction of lines that are not horizontal or vertical may easily be determined when the remainder of the sketch has been made.*

g. *Objects or parts of objects farther from the eye appear smaller than those near the eye. This appearance of equal distances to be smaller is called foreshortening.*

h. *Circles, other curves, and irregular shapes can best be sketched by first sketching an enclosing square, rectangle, or prism.*

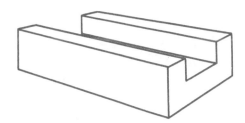

Fig. 202. Angular Perspective

Making a Parallel Perspective

1. Draw a fine light horizontal line to represent the horizon, Fig. 201. If the picture is to be below the horizon, locate the horizon line about two inches below the top of an 8½″ x 11″ space.

2. Draw the front face of the object, making the horizontal lines parallel with the horizon and the vertical lines of the object vertical in the sketch, Fig. 201. Keep all the lines of the drawing fine and light so that if it is desirable they may be erased quickly and easily.

3. Locate the center of vision at the center of the horizon line. This will be the vanishing point of the picture, Fig. 201.

4. From each upper corner of the front face draw light lines converging in the center of vision, *C.V.* These represent the receding horizontal lines of the object.

5. Locate the position and draw the horizontal line to represent the lines in the back of the object. In simple perspectives the proportions can satisfactorily be estimated by the eye with a little care and practice.

6. When all lines are in their correct form and location, darken the outlines of the object.

Making a Two-Point or Angular Perspective

1. Locate and draw a fine light line to represent the horizon line, Fig. 203.

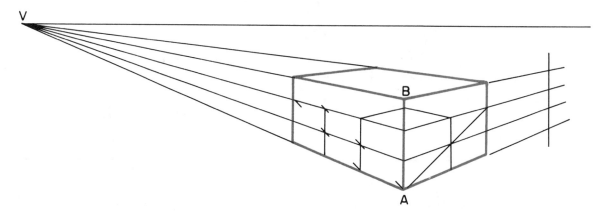

Fig. 203. Making an Angular Perspective

2. Locate the point in the picture nearest the eye, A, Fig. 203. This point should not be too far below the horizon line. One-third the height of the whole drawing space is about right.

3. Locate the vanishing points on the horizon line. These points should not be too close together. With one or two trials the vanishing point at the right and the one at the left can be so located as to give a pleasing picture.

4. From the point nearest the eye, draw fine, light lines to the vanishing points.

5. Sketch the nearest vertical lines of the object AB, making it the same height as the object or to scale.

6. From the upper end of the vertical height, B, sketch fine lines to the vanishing points.

7. On the receding lines at the top, estimate the width and length of the object in good proportion.

8. Sketch the receding lines at the top.

To determine the foreshortened measure on a receding line, a series of diagonals may be used as shown in Fig. 204.

1. Let us suppose that the object is one unit high and three and one-half units long. After determining the unit height, ab, draw the principal vanishing lines from the top and the bottom.

2. From the mid-way point, O, of the unit height, ab, sketch a line to the vanishing point, V.

3. Estimate the first foreshortened unit, bc, along the lower vanishing line and draw a vertical line.

4. Through the intersection of the center vanishing line drawn from o, and cd, draw the diagonal line b1 through 1, meeting the upper vanishing line at e. Draw the vertical line ef; ef and cf are the foreshortened unit measures of ab and bc. The distances fg and gk are obtained in the same manner.

5. A half of the foreshortened unit measure may be found by drawing the diagonals of a unit square. A vertical line drawn through their intersection determines half the unit measure.

Drawing a Circle in Perspective

A circle may be enclosed in a square as in Fig. 205.

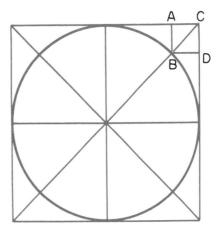

Fig. 205. Drawing a Circle in Perspective, First Step

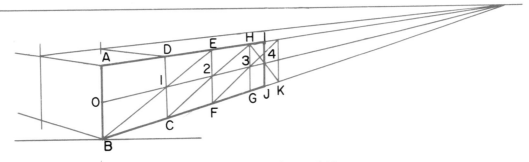

Fig. 204. Determining the Foreshortened Measure

1. Draw a square as in Fig. 205 and sketch a circle as true as you can.
2. Draw the enclosing square in perspective either in a vertical or horizontal position as in Fig. 206.
3. Draw the vertical and the horizontal diameters of the square in perspective.
4. Draw the diagonals of the square in perspective.
5. In Fig. 206 estimate the distance cd representing the projected distance cd in Fig. 205.
6. Draw parts of the vanishing line through d, Fig. 206, locating e and h on the diagonal.
7. Locate f and g in like manner.
8. Sketch the ellipse, which is the circle in perspective, through the ends of the diameters and the points e, f, g, and h.

If the circle is small or the draftsman has enough skill he can sketch the ellipse without locating the points on the diagonal.

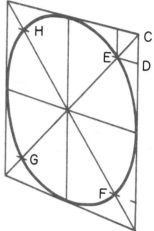

Fig. 206.   Drawing a Circle in Perspective, Second Step

PROBLEMS

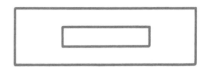

1. Make a cabinet drawing of a rectangular block 1½″ x 2″ x 3″.
2. Make a cabinet drawing of Problem 1 and Problem 2.
3. Make an isometric drawing of Problem 1.
4. Make an isometric drawing of Problem 2.
5. Make an isometric drawing of Problem 3.
6. Make a cabinet drawing of Problem 4.
7. Make an isometric drawing of Problem 4.
8. Make a parallel perspective of a plain rectangular box with butt joints and without a cover. The outside dimensions are: 7″ long, 4″ wide, and 3″ deep. The stock is to be ½″ thick.
9. Make a parallel or an angular perspective of any of the Problems 6 through 11. They are arranged in a relative order of complexity.
10. Make an angular perspective of Problem 5.
11. Make a parallel or angular perspective of Problem 4.
12. Make a cabinet drawing of Problem 12.
13. Make an isometric drawing of Problem 12.
14. These problems and any others in this book may be used in making drawings in any of the pictorial forms.

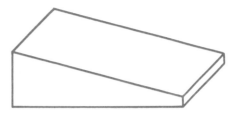

Problem 2 — Mortised Piece

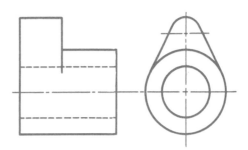

Problem 3 — Wedge

Problem 4 — Cam

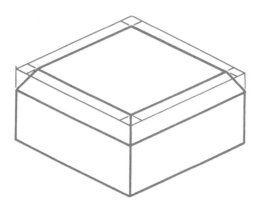

Problem 1 — Paper Weight

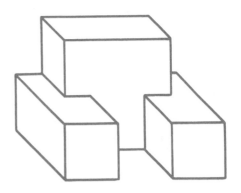

Problem 5 — Jig Casting

Problem 6 — Half Lap

Problem 9 — End Lap Joint

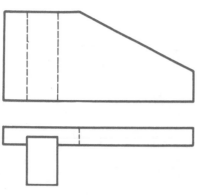

Problem 7 — Half Lap

Problem 10 — Gibbed Way

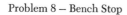

Problem 8 — Bench Stop

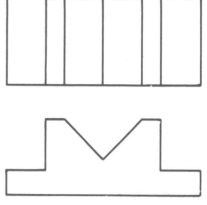

Problem 11 — V-Block

Problem 12: Shaft Bracket

Data:

A = $2\frac{1}{4}''$

B = $2\frac{3}{8}''$

C = $1\frac{7}{16}''$

D = $1''$

E = $\frac{7}{16}''$

F = $\frac{5}{8}''$ dia.

G = $\frac{3}{8}''$

H = $2''$

I = $1\frac{3}{4}''$

J = $\frac{3}{8}''$ dia.

K = $1\frac{1}{8}''$ dia.

Fillets, $\frac{1}{8}''$ radius

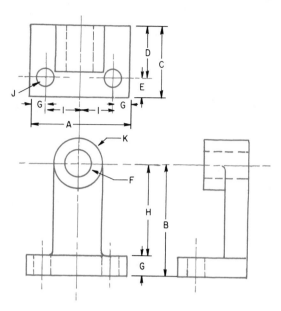

Problem 12 — Shaft Bracket

Sheet Metalworking and its Opportunities

Sheet metalworking has become one of the occupations for which highly trained men are in demand. Sheet metalworkers are employed in small establishments and in large factories. They are increasing in number because products made of sheet metal are also increasing. The work is concerned with sheets of metal; such as tin plate, galvanized iron, zinc, copper, lead, aluminum. The thicker sheets of metal, such as boiler plate, are classified as heavy sheet metal.

The products made of sheet metal are so numerous that a large book would be necessary to name them. A few of the products are heating and ventilating pipes, cooling chambers, furnaces, boilers, roof gutters, downspouts, cans of many kinds and for many purposes, water pails, automobile bodies, concrete forms, feeding troughs, grain storage bins, and water and gasoline tanks, toasters, waffle irons, toys, furniture, portable buildings, hangars, and garages.

Sheet metalworking is not new. It existed before 1620 in Bohemia. At that time the metal was made flat by hand. In 1865, in South Wales, a machine for rolling metal into sheets was invented. Today wherever sheet metal is made it is rolled into large sheets by machines that start with the large pieces of metal called ingots. Domestic sheet metal is made in the eastern part of the United States. About two-thirds of all sheet metal produced comes from Ohio, Pennsylvania, and West Virginia. A small quantity comes from Indiana and Maryland.

Nearly every city from the smallest to the largest in civilized countries has need for sheet metal and workers who are needed to change it to special forms. The latter are called *sheet metalworkers* and *tinners*. Spun and pressed aluminum is coming into use for small containers, replacing many of the uses for which other metals are now used.

Iron is more durable than steel for sheet metal. The black plates are *pickled* by dipping in sulphuric acid to remove dirt and scales. After the plates have been dipped in acid, they are washed, heated, and then dipped in molten tin, or tin and lead mixed. In making certain kinds of sheet metal, palm oil is used after the pickling process and after dipping in the molten lead-tin. A knowledge of chemistry of metals is helpful to those who control the making of sheet metal. Attempts to discover better methods and better plating are continually going on in the large industries.

When new products are to be manufactured, new processes call for installation of new machinery and alterations of plant layout. Spraying booths, guards for machinery, and blower sys-

A Sheet Metalworker

tems are some examples of the needs created by the new developments. A very large amount of this work requires the use of the heavier gage sheet metal or plates. The thickness varies from one-sixteenth to one-quarter inch and even thicker. The sheets or plates generally are made of steel and are uncoated. The joints ordinarily are riveted or welded.

The sheet metalworker must know a special form of drawing and must know how to perform a large number of hand and machine operations in shaping the metal. The period of learning is usually about four years or more, if one serves an apprenticeship; that is, if one learns from a skilled mechanic while working at the occupation. But in school he can learn it in about two years. The learning period varies with the ability and the dexterity of the learner. Modern vocational-technical schools are so operated that a learner can seek employment as soon as he is able to do all the work satisfactorily. Many schools have a definite understanding and arrangement with industry helping students to find employment upon completion of their training.

The average hourly wage for sheet metalworkers in 68 of the larger cities in America was $4.89 in 1966. There were about 55,000 sheet metalworkers in 1967. They are expected to increase rapidly in number through 1975 because

of the many new products that require sheet metal fabrication.[1] Opportunities for employment and advancement are excellent. A high school education is quite desirable for those who wish to enter this growing occupation. The study of sheet metal drafting is included in the training of sheet metalworkers.

The equipment used for changing sheet metal into various products is quite like that found in a sheet metal department of a school. A visit to a tinner or a heating and ventilating shop would reveal a large number of interesting machines.

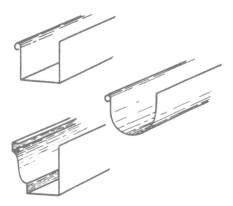

GUTTERS IN SHEET METAL

[1] Bureau of Labor Statistics, U.S. Department of Labor: Washington, D.C., 1968-69. Bulletin No. 1550.

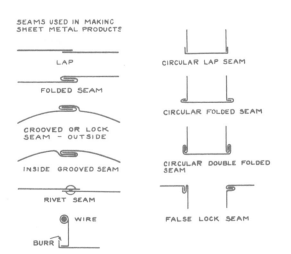

SEAMS USED IN MAKING SHEET METAL PRODUCTS

LAP

FOLDED SEAM

GROOVED OR LOCK SEAM - OUTSIDE

INSIDE GROOVED SEAM

RIVET SEAM

WIRE

BURR

CIRCULAR LAP SEAM

CIRCULAR FOLDED SEAM

CIRCULAR DOUBLE FOLDED SEAM

FALSE LOCK SEAM

Fig. 207. Seams Used in Making Sheet Metal Products

Fig. 208. Gutter Forms and Sheet Metal Products

These are machines that cut metal, bend and form it, make bends for special seams and make seams, make wire edges as on pails, and crimp special forms as on stovepipe elbows. In factories large machines are used to press the metal into desired forms as in auto body making.

Some of the common joints used in making sheet-metal products are shown in Fig. 207. A few sheet-metal products are shown in Fig. 208.

The type of drawing used in sheet-metal working is called sheet-metal drafting or lay-out. Basically it is a form of *surface development*. It is a branch of manufacturing employing many workers besides those who work in metal.

Surface developments also are applied to the layout of templates and dies in the manufacture of paper cartons, pasteboard boxes, fruit and vegetable baskets, folding purses and drinking cups. Hundreds of examples may be seen in drug and grocery stores and in the home. The methods of making surface developments also are applied in laying out awnings.

Making the Surface Development of a Prism

This is the first lesson in making the drawings that are used in occupations that you have just studied. You will see at once that knowledge of sketching and instrument drawing is quite necessary to make this form of drawing easy. There seem to be many lines to draw, but a study of the directions will prove how simple it is.

To make a *surface development* means to lay out the surfaces of an object so they can be seen in their true shapes and sizes and thus give the workman the information that he could not obtain from a two- or three-view dimensional drawing of the object. These surface developments are called patterns. The pattern for the cover of a baseball would be made by *surface development*. And so various objects in sheet-metal working, clothes in tailoring and dressmaking, cartons in paper box making, and objects in leather working require patterns in order to make them. Some provision must be made for fastening the sides and ends, either by gluing, soldering, riveting, or welding.

A *prism*, Fig. 209, is a form, either solid or void. The top and bottom of a prism are equal and parallel to each other, and its sides are *parallelograms*. A parallelogram is a figure whose opposite sides are parallel as shown in Fig. 210.

It is necessary to make surface developments of prismatic forms in making patterns of objects; such as boxes, trays, and envelopes to be made of paper, leather, or sheet metal. A length of

RECTANGULAR

OBLIQUE

HEXAGONAL

TRIANGULAR

PENTAGONAL

TRIANGULAR

Fig. 209. A Few Prisms

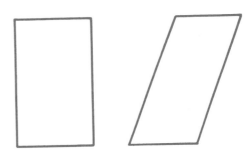

Fig. 210. Opposite Sides are Parallel in a Parallelogram

rectangular heating or ventilating pipe is prismatic in form. To make the development of an object of prismatic form, the following directions for developing a length of a small ventilating pipe, Fig. 211, will be helpful.

1. At one side of the sheet make a two-view dimensional drawing of the object, as in Fig. 211.
2. If the instructor plans to have you cut out the pattern, it will be unnecessary to make a sheet layout with title and border lines.
3. Draw two parallel lines by projecting them from the front view. Either one of these lines may be called a *stretchout* line.
4. Beginning at one end of one line, as at *A'* in Fig. 211, lay off with the dividers distances *A'B'*, *B'C'*, *C'D'*, and *D'C'* by transferring them from the proper views in the working drawing.
5. At points *B'*, *C'*, and *D'* draw vertical quarter-inch dash lines to mark the folding lines. They are called *break lines*.
6. In the shop a ⅜" flap is left on one end of the piece to be used in joining the ends with solder. If you plan to make a paper pattern to try out the development, you may leave a flap for pasting. Otherwise, you need not leave a flap. The workman will take care of that.
7. Study Fig. 212 and see how you would develop Fig. 211 if it were cut off at an angle and made into a filing box for cards.

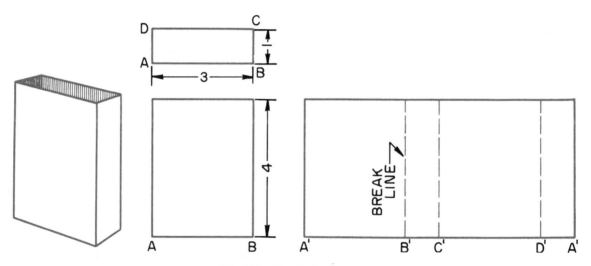

Fig. 211. Ventilating Pipe

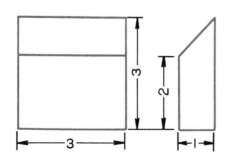
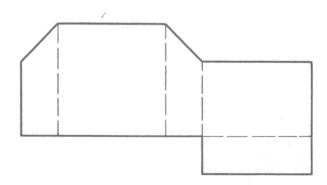

Fig. 212. Filing Box

Questions

1. Is it always necessary to project the pattern lines from the front view as shown in Fig. 211? In what other way can it be done?

2. Are there other forms for prisms than those shown in Fig. 209? Name as many as you can.

3. Name four objects, other than those listed, that are of prismatic form.

4. Examine a breakfast food container and then make a layout for an individual serving box with flaps for joining the sides and closing the top and bottom. Fold into shape and fasten joints along the side and bottom as a test of your layout.

Transferring a Triangle

Frequently in laying out patterns for leather, sheet metal, art metal, or paper cartons, it is necessary to transfer a triangle from one position to another. Here is the way it can be done quite easily. Two applications of this construction are given.

First Application

1. Let us suppose that triangle *ABC*, Fig. 213, is wanted in another position.

2. Lay off *AB*, Fig. 214, equal to *AB*, in Fig. 213.

3. With *A* as a center and *AC* as radius, draw an arc at *C*. Fig. 214.

4. With *B* as a center and *BC* as a radius, draw an arc cutting the first arc at point *C*.

5. Draw lines *AC* and *BC* and the triangle will be completed in its new position, Fig. 214.

Second Application

1. Suppose that *ABCD*, Fig. 215, which has four sides instead of three as in a triangle, must be transferred to a new position.

2. Draw the diagonal, *DB*, dividing the figure into two triangles. A plane figure of any shape can be divided into two or more triangles.

3. Lay off *DC*, Fig. 216, equal to *DC*, Fig. 215.

4. Construct triangle *DCB*, Fig. 216, equal to triangle *DCB*, Fig. 215, as in the first application.

5. Construct triangle *DBA*, Fig. 216, equal to *DBA*, completing the transfer of *ABCD* to its new position.

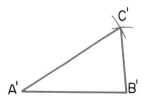

Fig. 213. Triangle to be Transferred

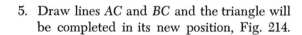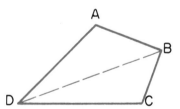

Fig. 215. Four-Sided Figure Divided into Triangles

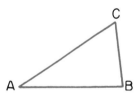

Fig. 214. New Triangle

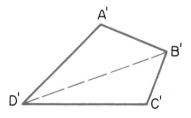

Fig. 216. Four-Sided Figure Transferred

Transferring an Angle

It is often necessary to transfer angles in making a drawing. The method for transferring angles is simple. It involves some of the same principles as transferring a triangle.

1. Let *ABC* be the angle to be transferred. Fig. 217.

2. With *B* as a center, and with any radius less than *AB*, draw the arc *XY* cutting lines *AB* and *BC*.

3. Draw one line *AB* of the new angle in its proper place.

4. With *B* as a center, draw the arc *XY* equal to arc *XY*.

5. Set the compasses to distance *XY*. With *X* as a center, draw an arc cutting arc *XY*.

6. Draw a straight line from *B* through *Y* and angle *ABC* will be equal to angle *ABC*.

Study Fig. 217 until you can transfer angles quickly and accurately.

Questions

1. Can you discover a way to make a triangle if you know the size of one angle and the length of the two adjacent sides?

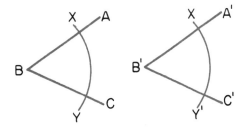

Fig. 217. To Transfer an Angle

PROBLEMS

Required: To make drawings of objects that involve developments of prismatic forms.

Problem 1:

Observe a paper carton made of corrugated paper board to discover how the layout is made and folded into shape. Try making a paper carton in which to mail a book 4¼″ x 6½″ x ¾″. A little allowance will be necessary for folding and packing.

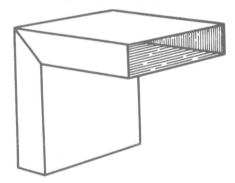

Problem 2 — Brad Box

Problem 2: Brad Box

Data:
3½″ x 3½″, ¾″ deep

Problem 3: Vent Pipe Elbow

Data:
90° elbow
Size of pipe, ½″ x 2″; length 2″
Show stretchout in one piece

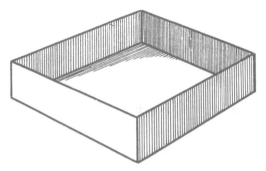

Problem 3 — Vent Pipe Elbow

Problem 4: Trinket Box

Data:
2″ x 2½″, 1½″ deep
Flap on cover, ⅝″ wide
Cover, $2\frac{1}{32}$″ x $2\frac{17}{32}$″

Problem 5: Dust Pan

Data:
Width, 9″
Height, 1½″
Length, 7″
Upper surface, 3″ wide
Break in bottom, 3½″ from back
Height of front edge, ½″
Width of handle, 1″
Width of handle opening, 1½″
Height of handle in the center, 2¼″, at back, 1½″

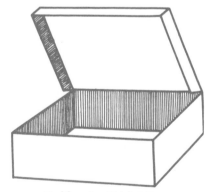

Problem 4 — Trinket Box

Problem 5 — Dust Pan

Making the Surface Development of a Pyramid

53

Pyramidal forms are found mostly in the more difficult sheet metal objects, such as ventilating pipes and heat register boxes. Pyramidal forms are seldom used alone, but they are combined with cylindrical and conical forms. A good example of a pyramidal form would be a pan or tray, square or rectangular in shape, with tapering sides as in Fig. 219.

The sides of a pyramid are triangles and the base may be any figure bounded by straight lines, Fig. 218.

The true lengths of all the lines are necessary in the making of patterns, and thus a new problem arises in drawing the patterns for a pyramidal form. When you made the patterns for the other forms, one of the views of the working

drawing gave the true lengths of the lines. But lines A in Fig. 220a may be in such position that you cannot determine their true length in either view. The full length of lines A can be found by making a simple change in one of the views.

Obtaining the True Length of a Line

1. Study Figs. 220a and 220b and compare the arrangement of the views. Lines A in Fig. 220 in both views have the appearance of being shorter than they really are, while lines A in Fig. 220b projected in the front view show full length. The radius for the development of a pattern could be taken from lines A in Fig. 220b, but neither of the lines in Fig. 220a could be used.

2. Note that the difference in the views that makes the full length of lines A possible is

Fig. 218. Pyramidal Forms

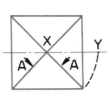
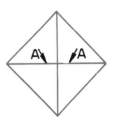

Fig. 219. Frustum of a Pyramid

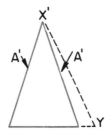

Fig. 220A. Pyramidal Form, Foreshortened Lines

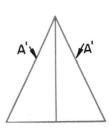

Fig. 220B. Pyramidal Form, True Length Lines

173

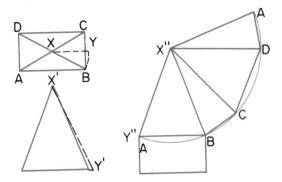

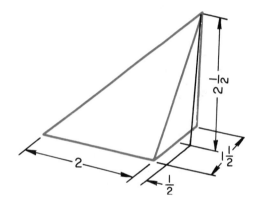

Fig. 220C. Development of Pyramidal Pattern

that the pyramid in Fig. 220b has been placed so lines A do not slant away from the eye. They are parallel to the picture plane for the front view. Place a pencil in these two positions and you will see the difference.

3. You need not draw all of Fig. 220b to obtain the true length of line A in Fig. 220a. Set the compasses to line A in the top view of Fig. 220a and with X as center revolve the line A into the horizontal position XY.

4. Project from Y to the extended base line of the front view at Y'. Connect points X' and Y' in the front view obtaining $X'Y'$ the true length of the line. Compare the length of line $X'Y'$ in Fig. 220c with that of line A in the front view of Fig. 220b.

Making the Pattern

1. After you have found the true length of line, you are ready to draw the pattern for a pyramid.

2. Set the compasses to distance XY in the front view and with center at X draw an arc. In Fig. 220c $X'Y'$ is the radius of the arc. On this arc set off the sides AB, BC CD, and DA in order.

3. Study Fig. 220c and apply what you know already about making patterns. You can make the pattern of the pyramid without additional instruction. Allow a ⅛″ flap for assembling.

4. Have your instructor check the pattern. Cut it out and assemble it.

5. Study Figs. 221a, 221b, and 221c and you can learn how to draw the surface development of an oblique pyramid. Your instruc-

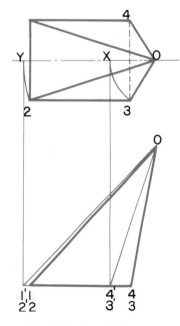

Fig. 221A. Problem

Fig. 221B. Pattern Layout

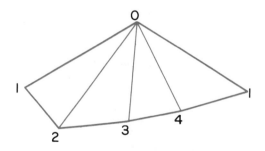

Fig. 221C. Completed Pattern

tor may want you to make a pattern for an object of this type.

Questions

1. Line $X'Y'$ in Fig. 220c is equal in length to line *A*. (True or False)
2. Study the following objects and make note of the lines that do not show true length. How would you obtain their true length to develop a pattern?
3. Name several objects that have a prism, cone, or pyramid in combination with another form. All four need not be in one piece. There may be only two or three in one object.
4. Is the object represented in *D* a solid or a hollow piece? How do you know?
5. Can you identify in *C* the top view of the line *F*?
6. In *E*, why is line *G* broken?

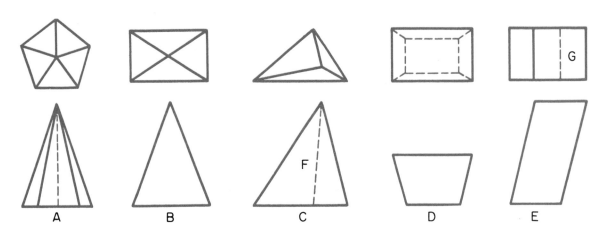

The Transition Piece of a Ventilator Pipe Involves
Pyramidal Forms

PROBLEMS

Required: To make drawings of objects that involve developments of pyramidal forms. In making the development of a problem requiring the transfer of a triangle, or of an angle, refer to Units 51 and 52.

Problem 1 — Pan

Problem 1: Pan

> *Data:*
> Bottom, 6″ x 8″
> Top, 6½″ x 8½″
> Depth, 1½″

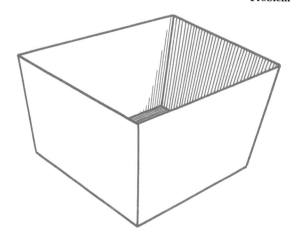

Problem 2: Form for Land Marker

> *Data:*
> Bottom, 8″ x 12″
> Top, 12″ x 18″
> Depth, 12″

Problem 2 — Form for Land Marker

Problem 3: Hood

> *Data:*
> Base, 1½″ x 2¼″
> Top, ⅝″ x ¾″
> Height of straight sections, ³⁄₁₆″
> Over-all height, 1″

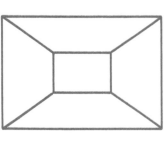

Problem 4: Transition Piece

> *Data:*
> Bottom, 1¾″ square
> Top, ¾″ square
> Height, 1⅝″
> Offset of top, 1″ center to center

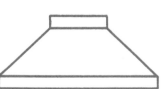

Problem 3 — Hood   Problem 4 — Transition Piece

Drawing a Five-Pointed Star (Pentagon)

Have you ever wished that you knew how to draw a star? To lay out a five-pointed star accurately, a circumference of the required size is divided into five equal parts. The same construction is used in drawing a regular pentagon. If it is desired to make several stars, they can be made from one construction.

1. Draw a circle of a diameter equal to the approximate size of the star that you need. Let *AB* and *CD* be the center lines, Fig. 222.
2. Bisect radius *OB* at point *E*. (See Unit 36.)
3. With radius *EC* and point *E* as a center, draw an arc cutting *AO* at *F*.
4. A radius equal to the distance *FC* will divide the circumference into five equal parts.
5. With the dividers set to distance *FC*, locate the five points on the circumference.
6. Draw the lines connecting the points as shown in Fig. 223 and darken the outline as in Fig. 224 and you will have the star.

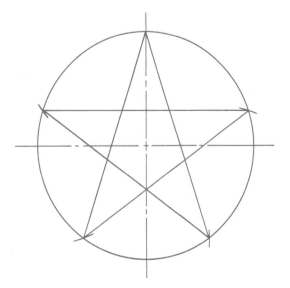

Fig. 223. Connecting Lines Drawn

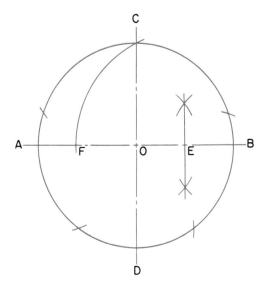

Fig. 222. Construction of a Pentagon

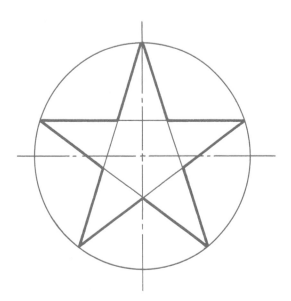

Fig. 224. Completed Star

7. If you want stars of different sizes, draw a line from each point of the star to the center O. With O as a center, draw a circle for each size of star that you desire. The radial lines cutting the circle will locate the points of the new star.

8. If you want a number of stars, transfer with carbon paper one of each size to a piece of cardboard. Cut the star from the card and use it as a pattern (template).

Questions

1. How would you locate the centers of five equally spaced holes on any given size circle?

2. Can you draw a pentagon — a plane figure with five equal sides and equal angles?

PROBLEMS

Problem 1:

Draw a pentagonal prism with one face squarely at the back. A pentagonal prism would make a unique column for an electric lamp.

Problem 2:

Draw a pentagonal pyramid with the top removed at an angle of thirty degrees to the horizontal. Make the diameter of enclosing circle of the base 2″ and the height of the original pyramid 4″.

55   Drawing Irregular Curves

Curved lines that cannot be drawn with compasses are drawn with an irregular or French curve, Fig. 225. Such lines are frequently necessary in sheet-metal drawing. Irregular curves are made of celluloid and may be purchased in a variety of shapes and sizes.

1. Lay out the points of the curve to be drawn. The distance between layout points is determined by the size of the curve. There should be enough points to make sure of a smooth curve, Fig. 226.

2. Sketch a line lightly through the points, making the curve smooth, as in Fig. 226.

3. To make the curve smooth, use the irregular curve as a guide. By trial select a portion

Fig. 225. There are Many Shapes of Irregular Curves

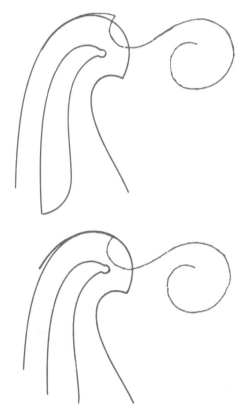

Fig. 226. Sketch a Line Lightly, Making Smooth Curves

Fig. 227. Fit the Curve to the Sketched Line

of the irregular curve that fits one end of the sketched curve as shown in Fig. 227. Draw the line a little shorter than is possible to make it with one position of the irregular curve.

4. Move the irregular curve, selecting another portion that accurately fits the sketched curve and a small part of that already drawn. Draw the line as before, making it not quite as long as is possible to make it.

5. Continue to move the curve and draw lines until the desired shape is completed.

6. Examine the line carefully to see that there are no kinks or breaks. Use the curve again on any part that needs smoothing.

7. When drawing symmetrical shapes in irregular curves, draw an axis first, Fig. 228. Fit the irregular curve carefully to a portion of the figure on one side of the axis. Mark with a pencil on the irregular curve the location of the ends of that part of the figure that fits the curve, at as *ab*, Fig. 228. Turn the irregular curve over and draw the line in a similar position on the other half of the figure.

Questions

1. In drawing irregular shapes make light (A) through which (B) lines are to be (C) before applying the (D).

2. Each portion of a line drawn with the irregular curve should go beyond the next point even though it may not touch the point. (True or False)

3. Why mark parts of the curve with a pencil when drawing lines of the same shape?

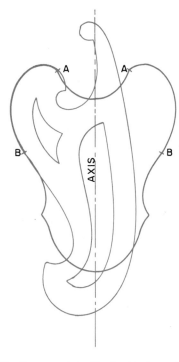

Fig. 228. Draw an Axis, Fit the Curve, and Mark the Ends as at "A" and "B"

Making the Surface Development of a Cylinder

In making the development of a prismatic object, you worked with straight lines. In making the development for a cylindrical form, you will draw curved lines. The prism has plane surfaces, and the cylinder has a continuous curved surface with a circular top and a circular bottom parallel to each other, as in pipe *A* in Fig. 229. Pipe *B* is a cylindrical form that has been made with one end slanting.

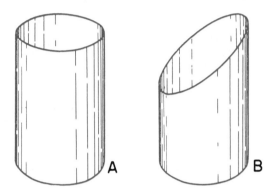

Fig. 229. Cylindrical Forms

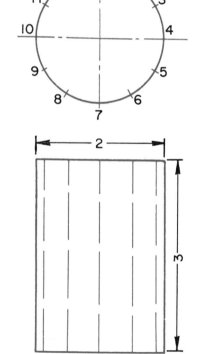

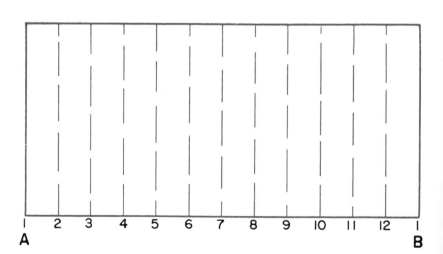

Fig. 230. Layout of Cylinder

1. On a separate sheet draw two views of pipe *A* as shown in Fig. 230.
2. Divide the end view into twelve equal parts using the 30°-60° triangle, Fig. 230.
3. Draw two parallel lines by projecting them from the front view, Fig. 230.
4. Set the dividers to distance *1-2* in the top view. Beginning at *A,* on the stretchout, lay off distance *1-2* twelve times, which is equal to the number of divisions in its circular view. This will give the length of the pattern that will be necessary to make the pipe of the desired circumference. Allow one-eighth inch for flap. In the shop, flaps would be left on both ends for a seam.
5. In arithmetic you learned that the circumference is equal to the diameter multiplied by 3.1416. This will be helpful in drawing patterns of cylindrical forms. For another suggestion see Unit 41. If your instructor

wishes to have you do so, cut out this pattern, assemble it, and check for proper size.

6. To draw a pattern for pipe *B* in Fig. 229, which is cut off at an angle, it would only be necessary to project the divisions from the top view to the front ivew as in Fig. 231. Then number them to match the numbers in the top view. Project the points across to the proper vertical lines on the pattern. For example, point *2* in the front view is projected to line *2* in the pattern. Through the points thus located on the pattern, sketch a line to form a curve and then smooth it with the French curve.
7. If you were to make a pipe elbow, it would be necessary only to make two of these patterns and join them as in Fig. 232. If you would lay out one pattern on a large piece of paper, the opposite side would form the matching piece of the elbow, Fig. 233.

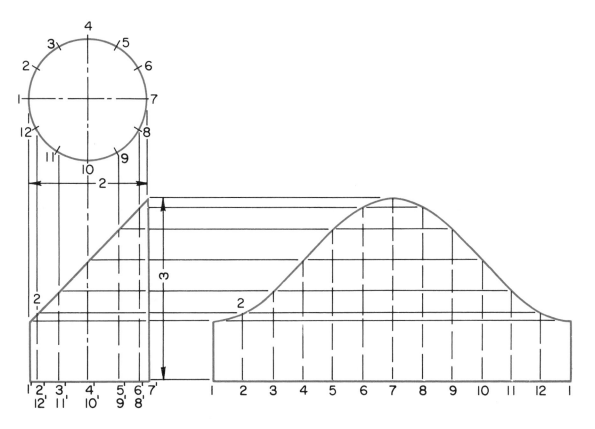

Fig. 231. Layout of Cylinder Cut at an Angle

Questions

1. Would smaller or larger divisions than those shown in the top view of Fig. 230 make the pattern more exact in length?
2. How can you check the length of the pattern to be sure that it will form a pipe of the right circumference?

3. Name several objects with cylindrical forms.

4. Examine a sheet metal pipe and make a sketch of the seam to see whether you have allowed enough flaps on your pattern.

5. Where will the seam come on part *A?* Where on part *B?*

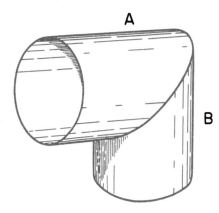

Fig. 232. Pipe Elbow

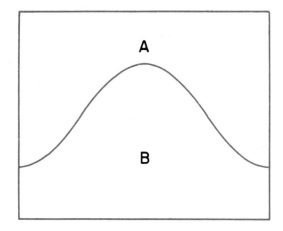

Fig. 233. Layout of Pipe Elbow

PROBLEMS

Required: To make drawings of objects that involve developments of cylindrical forms.

Problem 1: Cup

Data:
Diameter, 2½″
Height, 1½″
Handle, ⅝″ wide, designed as desired
Two tangent circular arcs are suggested

Problem 1 — Cup

Problem 2: Cookie Cutter

Data:
Diameter, 2¼″
Height, ⅞″
Hole in top of cutter, 1¼″
Width of handle, ⅞″; radius, 1¹⁄₁₆″

Problem 2 — Cookie Cutter

Problem 3: Scoop

Data:
Diameter, 2″
Length at bottom, 4″
Cutting angle, 45°
Width of handle, ⅝″
Radius of handle, ⅞″

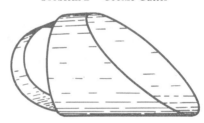

Problem 3 — Scoop

Problem 4: Candle Holder

Data:
Diameter, 3½″
Height at back, 5″; in front, ½″
Handle, ¾″ wide, designed to suit
Diameter of candle socket, ⅞″
Height, 1″
Position of socket, ½″ from back
Reverse curve of sides to be designed as desired

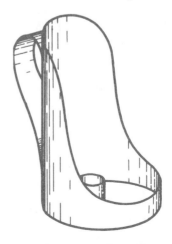

Problem 4 — Candle Holder

185

Conical forms are used extensively in sheet-metalworking. Funnels of various kinds, water pails, oil measures, and waste baskets are partly conical in form. In some way they contain in part the shape of the cone shown in Fig. 234. Note the shapes of the waste basket and the oil measure in Fig. 235. You will see that a cone has a round base and that its sides taper evenly to a point that is exactly over the center of the base. This fact makes the drawing of a pattern for a conical object rather simple. It is simpler than the many lines used in laying out the pattern make it appear. The method used in making a pattern for the cone in Fig. 234 can be applied in drawing other conical forms.

1. Draw two views of the cone, giving the necessary dimensions as in Fig. 236.

2. Divide the top view into twelve parts and number the points on the circumference as you did in making the pattern for the cylinder.

3. Observe in Fig. 236 that R, the slant height of the cone, is equal to R, the radius of the pattern. Set the compass to draw the radius R and draw arc AB for the pattern.

4. With the dividers set to distance 1-2 in the top view, lay off distance 1-2 twelve times on arc AB.

5. With straight lines, connect the starting point at A and the finishing point at B to the center of the arc at O and you will have the pattern for the sloping surface of the cone.

6. Study Fig. 237 and you can learn how to draw the development for a pan with sloping sides or any object that has the form of a truncated cone.

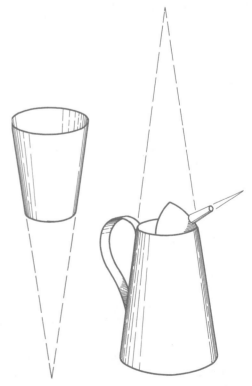

Fig. 235. There are Many Conical Forms

Fig. 234. Cone

Questions

1. How could you increase the number of divisions for laying off the length of the pattern to 16 or 24?

2. In the front view, (A) is equal to (B) in the pattern.

3. The circumference of the cone is equal to (A) times the (B).

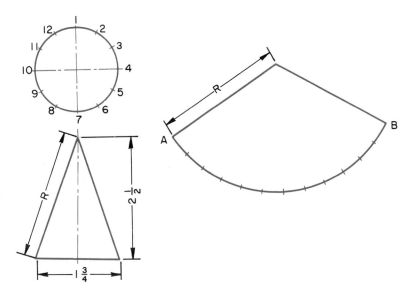

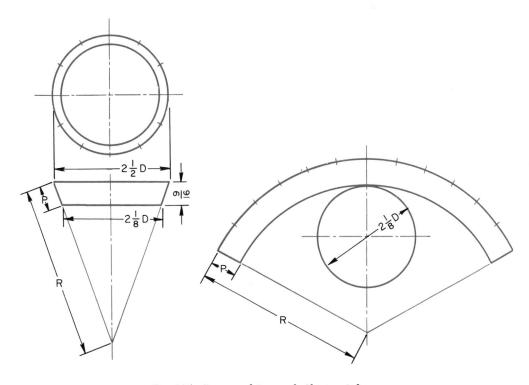

Fig. 236. Layout of Cone

Fig. 237. Layout of Pan with Sloping Sides

PROBLEMS

Required: To make drawings of objects that involve developments of conical forms.

Problem 1 — Pan

Problem 1: Pan

Data:
Diameter of rim, 2¾″
Diameter of bottom, 2½″
Vertical height, ⁹⁄₁₆″

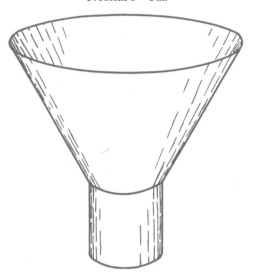

Problem 2: Motor Funnel

Data:
Diameter at top, 3¼″
Diameter of cylindrical part, 1″
Over-all height, 2⅝″
Height of cylindrical part, 1″

Problem 2 — Motor Funnel

Problem 3: Oil Funnel

Data:
Height of upper part, 1½″
Over-all height, 3″
Diameter at top, 2¾″
Diameter at joint, ⅞″
Diameter at bottom, ⁹⁄₁₆″

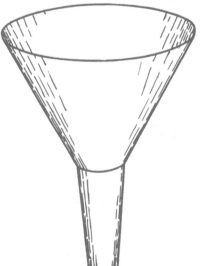

Problem 4: Transition Piece

Data:
Height of upper section, ½″
Height of lower section, ⅜″
Diameter of bottom, 2″
Diameter at top, 1″
Over-all height, 3″

Problem 3 —
Oil Funnel

Problem 4 —
Tranisition Piece

Opportunities in Electrical Working

58

When Edison invented the incandescent lamp, countless opportunities began to open for invention and for work in the world of electricity. It is said that Benjamin Franklin opened the way to electricity in this country with his key and kite string, even though people gave very little thought to it at the time. Alexander Graham Bell cleared the way for public belief in electricity and its possible uses by his successful efforts with the telephone. And Marconi gave to the world

Building the Electrical Power Generator for the Norris Dam
(Courtesy, Westinghouse Electric and Manufacturing Company)

the radio which, in its seeming magic, has opened an entirely new field of engineering in electricity.

Let us look about the home. With the incandescent lamp, telephone, radio, and television, there is the refrigerator, washer, ironer, dryer, heater, incinerator, and many other things to accompany them, and more coming. Then consider the automobile and the many electrical features that go with it.

There also is the field of public utilities which includes street cars and general electrical power service, besides the telephone and telegraph, that depend almost entirely on various aspects of electrical production.

In building construction there is constant need for electrical installation and upkeep. The many home appliances must be maintained. The electrical manufacturing plants are constantly designing and selling new machines and devices. There must be a great army of workers to produce and repair the few applications of electricity just mentioned. It is practically impossible to list all the jobs involved.

Perhaps there is nothing in our industrial history that has developed as rapidly as radio and television. Engineers tell us, that even though we now have what seems to be perfected reception, there are many improvements coming.

There is work of some kind in the electrical field in which persons sixteen years or older can find employment. There seems to be no old age limit. Training and experience are factors that have much to do with the kind of employment and advancement that the individual may secure. However, even for the more simple types of work, more and more emphasis is being placed on high school education. Ability in mechanical drawing and blueprint reading seems to be necessary for success at this work along with knowledge of electricity.

The broad achievements and greater opportunities of advancement for persons interested in electricity are in electrical engineering. It is one of the more difficult professions and it requires an excellent grounding in mathematics and science beginning with courses in high school. For those who have the willingness and stick-to-it-iveness, as well as the ability, there is open a wide door of opportunity in engineering. But, for those who cannot study engineering, there are lesser and very interesting opportunities with good pay. Courses in drawing and electricity are useful whether one goes to college or enters the electrical field as a mechanic.

Wages in electrical work vary more than in any other activity. Even in engineering the salaries vary widely. However, the really high pay seems to be in engineering, where it is possible to earn several thousands dollars a year. It would seem wise, therefore, not to attempt to list the wages paid in the many electrical engineering and electrical workers' specialities as is possible with many occupations. Generally, the opportunities and the wages are among the highest in industry.

Training for electrical work can be had in many ways. Technical schools are open to persons of sixteen years and older in which various phases of training in electrical work are available. Some large corporations have their own training schools in which training is offered in electrical work as well as in other occupations. Some of the large technical high schools throughout the country offer excellent courses leading to electrical engineering. Nearly every university in the nation offers training leading to degrees in electrical engineering.

While electrical engineering is exceedingly interesting, there are many difficulties for those who lack the preparation that leads to independent development. For those who would strive to reach the top, there is much encouragement. It is said that the big achievements in electricity are still ahead.

Electrical Drawing

Unit

59

Electrical drawing is the language of the electrical engineer and the electrician. The nature of the materials used in construction makes it necessary to rely on symbols for expressing the meanings intended. Some of the symbols in house planning are those used in electrical drawing. Mechanical drawing and sketching form the foundation for making electrical drawings. In fact, if one has had general experience in drawing, he will only need to learn the symbols and understand electricity in order to make electrician's diagrams. Electrical engineers also have need for working drawings of machinery.

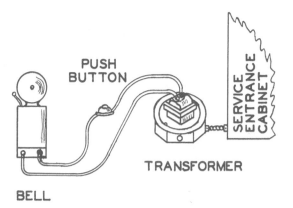

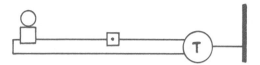

Fig. 239. Electrical Circuit, Line Power

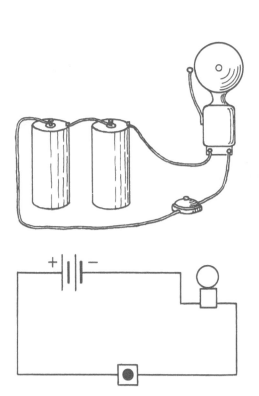

Fig. 238. Electrical Circuit, Battery Power

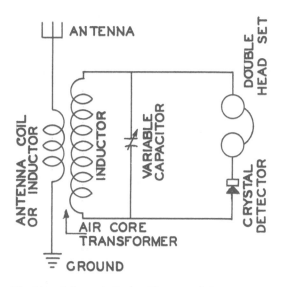

Fig. 240. Schematic Circuit Using Symbols to Represent Electrical Components

Making Diagrams

1. For all practical purposes a good line sketch will be satisfactory for a diagram. However, if considerable use is to be made of the diagram, a blueprint of an instrument drawing would be very desirable. A sketch would be necessary as the first step in making a wiring diagram.

2. Study the electrical symbols used in the phase of electrical work for which you are making a drawing. If a house wiring diagram is desired, use the symbols for house wiring. If a radio diagram is desired, refer to the symbols for radio, Fig. 243. For an advanced study of electrical symbols refer to the bulletin *Standards of the American Institute of Electrical Engineers*. (A.I.E.E., 33 W. 29th St., New York City)

3. Study Figs. 237 and 238 and observe how the symbols are used to represent the various parts of an electrical circuit. Note that the relation of the parts is more important than the scale in such a sketch.

4. Have your sketch approved before proceeding with the wiring or before making an instrument drawing, if one is to be made.

Questions

1. Why is the placement of parts in relation to each other more important than the scale?

2. Would there be difficulty in wiring if the symbols were not placed exactly as shown in the sample diagrams even though the relation of parts remained the same?

3. Name five occupations that require knowledge of electricity.

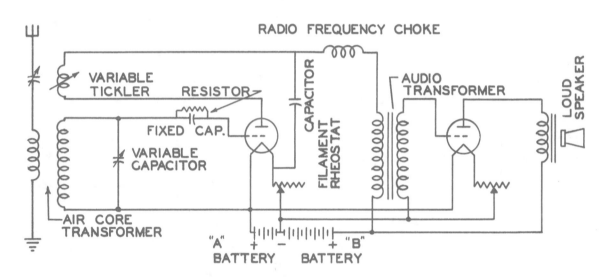

Fig. 241. Schematic of a Receiving Circuit

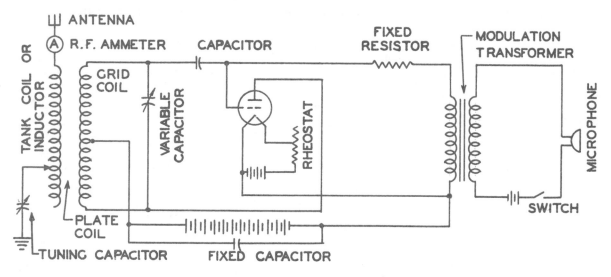

Fig. 242. Schematic of a Transmitting Circuit

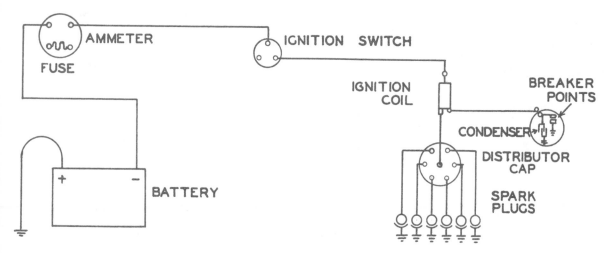

Fig. 243. Primary and Secondary Circuits in a Six Cylinder Automobile

ELECTRICAL SYMBOLS

GENERAL OUTLETS

	Ceiling	Wall
Outlet	○	-○
Blanked Outlet	Ⓑ	-Ⓑ
Drop Cord	Ⓓ	-Ⓓ
Electrical Outlet	Ⓔ	-Ⓔ

For use only when circle alone might be confused with columns, plumbing, etc.

Fan Outlet	Ⓕ	-Ⓕ
Junction Box	Ⓙ	-Ⓙ
Lampholder	Ⓛ	-Ⓛ
Lampholder with pull switch	Ⓛ$_{PS}$	-Ⓛ$_{PS}$
Pull Switch	Ⓢ	-Ⓢ
Clock Outlet Specify voltage	Ⓒ	-Ⓒ

CONVENIENCE OUTLETS

Duplex Convenience Outlet	⊖
Convenience Outlet other than duplex 1 - single, 3 - triplex	⊖$_{1,3}$
Weatherproof Convenience Outlet	⊖$_{WP}$
Range Outlet	⊜$_R$
Switch and Convenience Outlet	⊖$_S$
Radio and Convenience Outlet	⊖-Ⓡ
Floor Outlet	⊙
Special Purpose Outlet (Des. in Spec.)	⬤

SWITCH OUTLETS

Single Pole Switch	S
Double Pole Switch	S$_2$
Three Way Switch	S$_3$
Four Way Switch	S$_4$
Automatic Door Switch	S$_D$
Electrolier Switch	S$_E$
Key Operated Switch	S$_K$
Switch and Pilot Lamp	S$_P$
Circuit Breaker	S$_{CB}$
Weatherproof Circuit Breaker	S$_{WCB}$
Momentary Contact Switch	S$_{MC}$
Remote Control Switch	S$_{RC}$
Weatherproof Switch	S$_{WP}$

SPECIAL OUTLETS

Any Standard Symbol as given here may, with the addition of a lower case letter, be used to designate some special variation of standard equipment of particular interest in a specific set of architectural plans.

○$_{a,b,c,etc.}$
⊖$_{a,b,c,etc.}$
S$_{a,b,c,etc.}$

When used, they must be listed in the key of symbols on each drawing and if necessary further described in the specifications.

SPECIAL AUXILIARY OUTLETS

Subscript letters refer to notes on plans or detailed description in specifications.

□$_{a,b,c,etc.}$

AUXILIARY SYSTEMS

Push Button	▫
Buzzer	◻/
Bell	◻
Annunciator	◇
Outside Telephone	◀
Interconnecting Telephone	◁
Bell Ringing Transformer	Ⓣ
Electric Door Opener	Ⓓ
Maid's Signal Plug	Ⓜ
Radio Outlet	Ⓡ
Interconnection Box	▭
Battery	⑊⑊⑊

Auxiliary System Circuits
Note: Any line without further designation indicates a 2-wire system. For a greater number of wires, designate with numerals in manner similar to — 12 No. 18 in ¾″ C., or designate by number corresponding to listing in schedule.

MISCELLANEOUS

Control Center	▬
Branch Circuit, Concealed in ceiling or wall	——
Branch Circuit, Concealed in floor	— — —
Branch Circuit, Exposed	- - - - -
Home Run. Number of circuits shown by number of arrows.	⇥

Note: Any circuit without further designation indicates a 2-wire circuit. For a greater number of wires indicate as follows:

3 Wires	⫻
4 Wires	⫻

Feeders
Use heavy lines and designate by number corresponding to listing in feeder schedule.
▬

(The above symbols are in accordance with ASA . . . 432.2-1954.)

[1]A. Carl Bredahl, Westinghouse Home Wiring Handbook, pp. 102-103. Pittsburg: Westinghouse Electric Corp., 1946.

RADIO DIAGRAM SYMBOLS

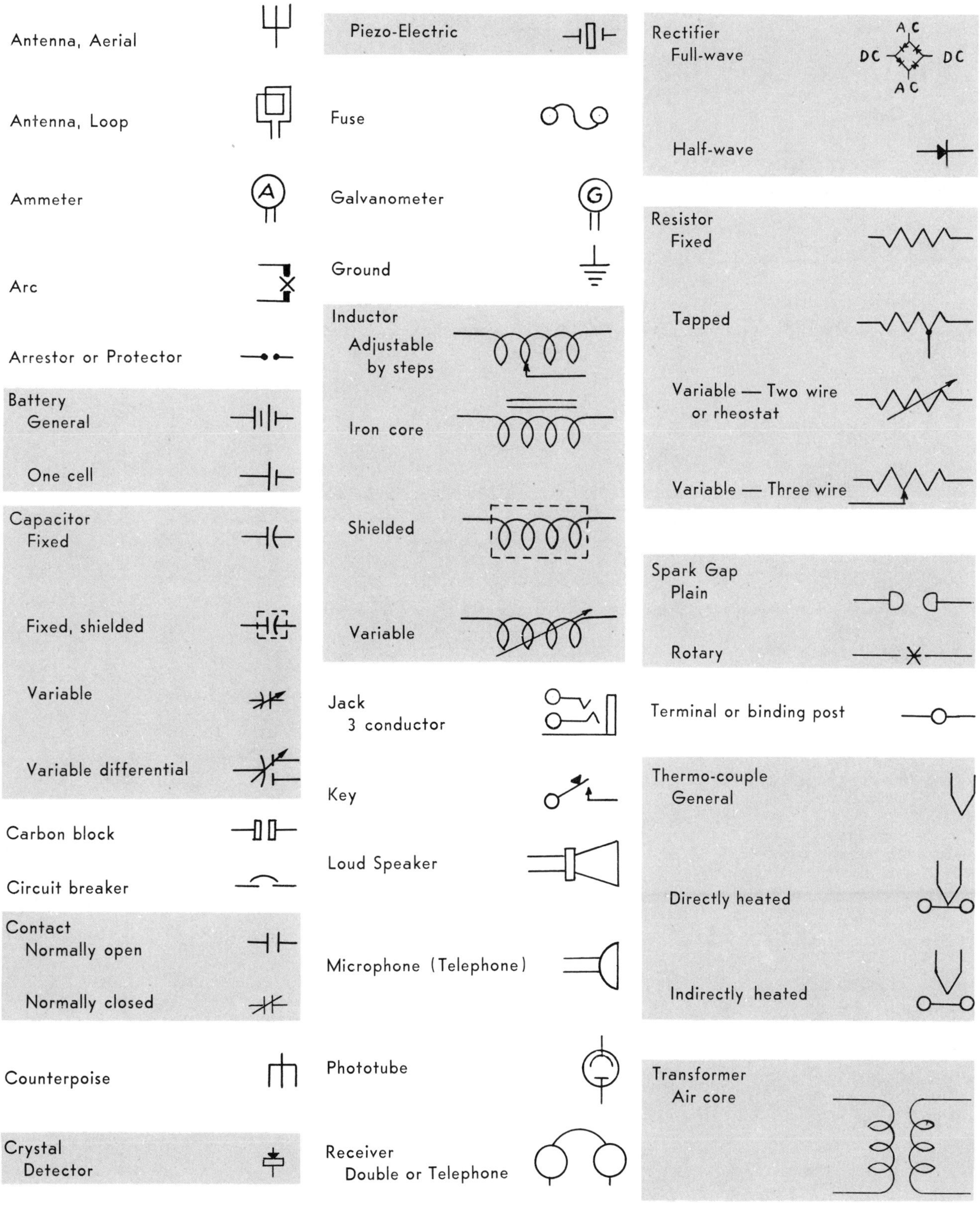

Antenna, Aerial

Antenna, Loop

Ammeter

Arc

Arrestor or Protector

Battery
General

One cell

Capacitor
Fixed

Fixed, shielded

Variable

Variable differential

Carbon block

Circuit breaker

Contact
Normally open

Normally closed

Counterpoise

Crystal
Detector

Piezo-Electric

Fuse

Galvanometer

Ground

Inductor
Adjustable
by steps

Iron core

Shielded

Variable

Jack
3 conductor

Key

Loud Speaker

Microphone (Telephone)

Phototube

Receiver
Double or Telephone

Rectifier
Full-wave

Half-wave

Resistor
Fixed

Tapped

Variable — Two wire
or rheostat

Variable — Three wire

Spark Gap
Plain

Rotary

Terminal or binding post

Thermo-couple
General

Directly heated

Indirectly heated

Transformer
Air core

°The symbols in this table have been made to conform to the American Standard — Graphical Symbols for Telephone, Telegraph, and Radio Use, ASA Standard Y32.2-1954.

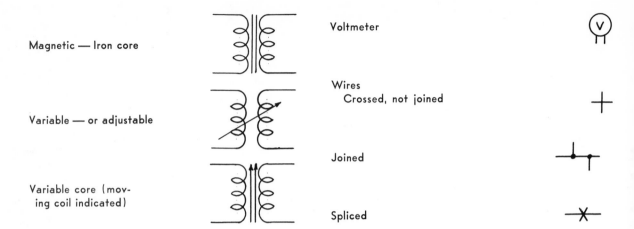

Magnetic — Iron core

Variable — or adjustable

Variable core (moving coil indicated)

Voltmeter

Wires
   Crossed, not joined

Joined

Spliced

PROBLEMS

Make a wiring diagram for:

1. A two bell and two-button circuit with three dry cells.

2. A two bell and two button circuit with a transformer.

3. A bell and buzzer circuit with a transformer for a front and rear door.

4. Study Figs. 240, 241, 242, and 243 and make a radio receiving diagram or a radio telephone transmitting diagram or an automobile ignition circuit.

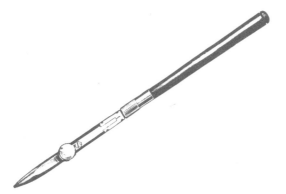

Inking a Drawing

Pencil drawings are satisfactory for limited use. For long service, a drawing should be inked; or still better, it should be made into a blueprint by first carrying the work through a tracing process with ink or pencil. In this unit you will learn how to ink. Later you will have an opportunity to learn how a blueprint is made. Inking is interesting and it is readily learned, although careful observance of the following directions is necessary.

Fig. 244. A Ruling Pen

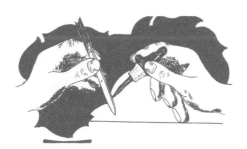

Fig. 245. Filling the Ruling Pen with Ink

Inking With a Pen

1. The ruling pen, Fig. 244, is used for inking straight and irregular curved lines. If you first learn to use the ruling pen properly, you will have acquired an ability that is very necessary to good inking.

2. To fill the pen with ink, hold the pen and the quill in position as shown in Fig. 245. A quill or glass dropper for filling the pen is fastened to the stopper of the ink bottle. Observe that the little finger of the hand that holds the quill rests on the table.

3. Dip the quill in the ink and then insert the quill between the nibs of the pen leaving about $\frac{3}{16}''$ of ink. If too much ink is placed in the pen, its weight will make it flow too fast and thus make a blot. See that no ink is left on the outside of the pen.

4. When inking with the ruling pen, use a T square or a triangle as a guide, in the same manner as when penciling.

5. Try the pen for size of line on the waste margin of the paper. Set the nibs for making the desired line by turning the adjusting nut with the thumb and second finger of the hand that holds the pen. In Fig. 246 is shown

Fig. 246. Using the Ruling Pen

the position for holding the pen so you can adjust it while testing. Observe that the adjusting nut is held away from the body.

6. Hold the straightedge slightly away from the line, and hold the pen on the line and against the top of the straightedge as shown in Fig. 247. See that the pen is perpendicular to the drawing board with both nibs touching the paper but leaning slightly in the direction of the line. Fig. 248. Let the hand rest on the third and fourth fingers as it moves along.

7. Use a free arm movement until the pen is near the end of the line. Then finish the line with a finger movement. When the end is reached, lift the pen quickly by raising the first and second fingers.

8. Whatever kind of line you are inking, be sure that it is kept uniform in width throughout the drawing. This can be done by resting the pen lightly on the paper and holding it against the straightedge without using pressure. Also, clean the pen frequently, and refill it, to prevent dirt and dried ink from collecting between the nibs. If dirt is allowed to collect, the nibs will gradually close up, and at the same time change the width of the line.

9. To prevent spreading the ink, promptly slide the straightedge away after the end of the line is reached.

10. Ink all horizontal lines by beginning with those at the top and working toward the bottom. Ink all vertical lines by beginning at the left and working toward the right.

11. Before rearranging the instruments and continuing with the inking of other parts of the drawing, be sure that all previously inked lines are dry.

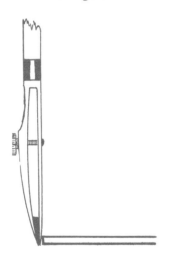

Fig. 247. Hold the Pen Against the Top of the Straightedge and Perpendicular to the Board

Fig. 248. Let the Pen Lean Slightly, with the Hand Resting Lightly on the Third and Fourth Fingers

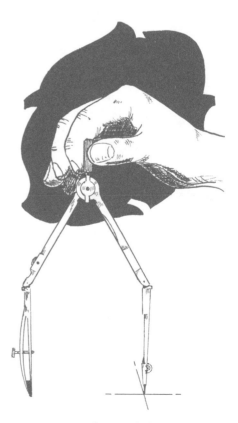

Fig. 249. Inking, with the Compasses

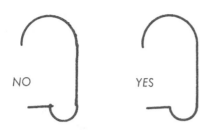

Fig. 250. Lines Must Meet Perfectly

Inking With Compasses

1. Arcs and circles are inked with the compasses. Fill the nibs of the compasses with ink in the same manner as in filling the ruling pen; and likewise, keep the compasses clean.

2. Instructions for using the pencil compasses also apply when using the ink compasses. Both legs of the compasses should be perpendicular to the paper, and both nibs of the pen should touch the paper, Fig. 249. See that the compasses lean slightly in the direction in which the lines are being drawn.

3. When arcs and circles and straight lines meet, they must meet perfectly. See Fig. 250. Remember that a line represents a surface and if there is a break in a line, it tells the workman that there is a break in the surface. Inaccurate work by the draftsman suggests to the workman that he, too, can do inaccurate work.

Order of Inking a Working Drawing

1. Ink all small circles and then the large ones. Then all arcs of circles.

2. Hidden object lines in circles and arcs of circles.

3. Irregular curves.

4. Horizontal lines, beginning at the top of the drawing.

5. Vertical lines, beginning at left of the drawing.

6. Inclined lines.

7. Center lines.

8. Dimension and extension lines.

9. Dimension figures and arrowheads.

10. Section lines.

11. Notes and record strip.

12. Border lines.

13. Check the drawing.

Questions

1. Fill the ruling pen by dipping it in the ink as you do a writing pen. (True or False)

2. Put about (A) of ink in the pen.

3. In inking, keep the straightedge: (1) on the pencil line, (2) slightly removed from the pencil line, (3) to the left of the line, (4) inclined toward the line.

4. Ink all guide lines for lettering. (True or False)

5. To erase a blot or an inked line first spread it with the finger, then use: (1) an ink eraser, (2) a knife, (3) a pencil eraser, (4) fine sandpaper, (5) a blotter.

6. What is the correct position for the nibs of the ruling pen in relationship to the surface of the paper?

7. What caused the difficulty with these lines?

Making a Tracing

A tracing must first be made of a drawing before there can be a blueprint. The tracing serves in the same way in blueprinting as does a negative in making pictures. The drawing is copied or *traced* with black ink or pencil on cloth or paper especially treated with starch to make it transparent. When the tracing has been completed, it is used in making blueprints.

Although pencil tracings do not make as clear blueprints as do ink tracings, many industries use pencil entirely for making tracings. Paper tracings are made for temporary use. In industry original drawings are frequently made in pencil either on pencil tracing cloth or on tracing paper. These serve as tracings from which blueprints are made and eliminate a step in the preparation of blueprints.

Tracing cloth is made of a fine quality of cotton fabric. The starch treatment renders it transparent as well as suitable for drawing. One surface is dull and the other is glazed. Most draftsmen trace on the dull side because it takes ink and pencil more readily than does the glazed side. Tracing cloth is used in industry more than tracing paper for making lasting tracings.

There are two kinds of tracing paper. One is common thin paper especially made so it is transparent. The other is called *vellum*. Vellum is paper, but it has been treated with oil so it looks quite like tracing cloth. It is very satisfactory for making tracings and it is less costly than tracing cloth, although the blueprints made with it are not as clear and sharp as those made with the cloth.

The instructional unit on inking will be of help to you in making a tracing. In industry most of the inking is done only when making tracings. A pencil drawing on paper is seldom inked. Tracing cloth is affected easily by moisture and,

therefore, it should be protected from water or moisture from the hands either while it is being traced or in storage.

Tracing on Cloth

1. Cut a piece of tracing cloth to a size about a half inch larger than the sheet to be traced.

2. Examine the piece thus cut. If there is a red thread near the edge of it, tear it off. This thread marks the selvage. If it is left on an edge of a piece of cloth, uneven shrinking and wrinkling takes place.

3. Fasten the upper left corner of the cloth in position over the drawing.

4. See that the cloth covers the drawing fully. Stretch it carefully to the lower right corner as you did in fastening the drawing sheet. Fasten it securely.

5. Stretch the cloth to the upper right and lower left and fasten as before. Smooth out any wrinkles by resetting the corner that needs it.

6. Dust chalk lightly over the whole tracing, and wipe it off with a clean cloth. This removes a slightly oily surface that tends to make the surface difficult to ink. No chalk should be left on the surface, however, because it will clog the pen when inking.

7. Place a sheet of paper over parts of the tracing not being inked in order to keep hand moisture off the surface.

8. Proceed to ink in the proper order for inking a drawing. Ink all lines in the conventional forms, except guide lines that show through the cloth from the drawing underneath.

9. Before lettering, trace with pencil on the cloth all guide lines for lettering so they can

be readily followed. Guide lines on the original drawing are difficult to follow through the tracing. Lettering is best done in tracing by not attempting to follow the lettering underneath too closely.

10. If a line or blot must be erased, proceed as you learned previously in the unit on erasing.

11. As the cloth gets out of shape easily, plan to trace all the views, or at least one view, completely before work must be stopped for the day.

12. If necessary to continue the work at a later time, loosen two corners on one side of the tracing. Cover the sheet with paper to protect it and lay the board away in the place provided for it.

13. When you have completely traced the whole drawing, check it to see that nothing has been omitted, then have your instructor approve it.

Tracing on Paper or Vellum

1. Fasten the paper or vellum to the board in the same way as in fastening cloth.

2. Proceed with the inking just as you did in tracing on cloth.

Tracing With Pencil

1. If a pencil tracing is to be made, use an H to 3H pencil and trace as in inking. Keep a sharp point on the pencil, and rotate it between the thumb and fingers to produce uniform lines.

2. The original drawing may be made on tracing paper if desired.

Questions

1. The lines on a tracing should follow exactly the conventional lines of working drawings. (True or False)

2. Oily fingers will make the surface of a tracing repel ink; therefore, the drawing surface should be protected with paper where it is not being inked. (True or False)

3. The order of tracing would be the same as in the order of inking a working drawing. (True or False)

4. Ink lines on tracings are erased satisfactorily with an ink eraser. (True of False)

Making a Blueprint

Blueprints are used by home craftsmen, skilled workers, engineers, architects — in fact, all kinds of people in many occupations and in all kinds of places where things are planned and made. In industry, any drawing whether blue, black, or brown is often called a *blueprint*.

A blueprint has a blue background with white lines and lettering and is made by using a tracing, blueprint paper, and a printing machine or some other printing device to hold the tracing and the paper in contact while being exposed to light, Fig. 251. As many blueprints as desired can be made from one tracing just as several pictures can be made from one negative. Prints are also made with black or brown lines on a white background. The blueprints are still much in use, so the process of making them is described in this lesson.

A tracing is made of the original drawing with either ink or pencil on translucent (partially transparent) cloth or paper. An original drawing can also be made on tracing paper or pencil cloth and used the same as any tracing for reproducing a drawing. The back of the tracing is placed against the chemically treated, sensitized surface of the blueprint paper and exposed to light.

Blueprint paper is white paper chemically treated. Before exposure, the sensitized side is light green in color. After exposure, it is gray-green. The parts of the paper covered by the black lines of the drawing turn white and the other portions turn blue when the exposed paper is given a bath in water. This is called a wet process. Brown-line and brown prints are made by a similar wet process; black and white prints are made by a moist process; and diazo prints (background white, lines dark) are dry developed, Fig. 251A.

Blueprint paper may be purchased in different "speeds," meaning that different amounts of exposure are required for printing. A thirty-second paper needs only thirty seconds in direct sunlight for exposure. And so one-minute and two-minute papers require one and two minutes respectively for exposure. The speed is indicated on the package and it is supposed to be timed for mid-day sunlight.

Fig. 251. Blueprint Frames for Sunlight Prints

Fig. 251A. Table Model Printer
(Courtesy, Eugene Dietzgen Company)

Blueprints can be made by electric machine or by sunlight. There are many types of machines and they all operate differently, but the general idea of making a blueprint is the same whether it is made by machine or by sunlight.

1. In Fig. 251 is shown an early blueprinting frame for sunlight printing. It is now quite obsolete, but in the absence of modern elec-

Fig. 252A. Continuous Blueprinting Machine

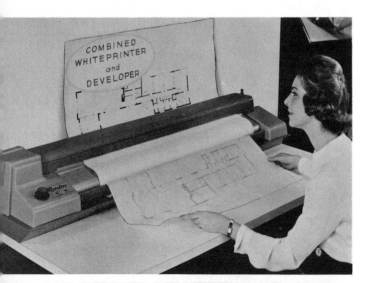

Fig. 252B. Diazo Machine (Courtesy, Rotolite Sales Corporation)
It prints and develops in one step, can be mounted on the wall or placed on a table, and may be considered one of the simplest of dry copy machines. It is equipped with a speed control.

tric equipment one can still make satisfactory prints on this type of frame. Many such frames are still in use. It has four parts — the frame, glass, felt pad, and a back that fastens snugly in place. Since it shows clearly what must be done to expose the blueprint paper, its use is described in detail.

2. Remove the back and felt pad under it. Clean the glass so nothing will obstruct the light.

3. Lay the tracing in the frame so the inked side is against the glass.

4. Cut the blueprint paper in a room in which the light is subdued.

5. Lay the blueprint paper on the tracing with the sensitized side down. Be sure that the tracing is fully covered with the blueprint paper.

6. Lay the felt on the paper and smooth it out evenly.

7. Place the back in position and clamp it. If the back has two parts, one side can be opened at a time to see that the paper is in place. The back should be firmly in place when clamped so it forces the pad against the paper and thus makes a perfect contact between the tracing and blueprint paper.

8. Place the frame in direct sunlight, or in strong electric light.

9. After exposure, wash the blueprint paper for five minutes in clean running water and hang it up to dry. The lines will become white and the background will become bright blue.

10. If the print is too light (under-exposed) or, if the lines seem gray or "burned out" from "over exposure," different chemicals may be placed in the rinsing bath to make the print bright blue and the lines pure white. An ounce of sodium bichromate or potassium bichromate to a gallon of rinse water will save the print. Hydrogen peroxide or dioxygen can also be used. It will be necessary to wash the blueprint again after the chemical treatment.

11. The full process just explained is carried out to a finished blueprint with a machine such as shown in Fig. 252A.

Questions

1. When the tracing is placed properly in the frame, the lettering on the drawing should read backwards from the glass side of the frame. (True or False)

2. Blueprints can be made in (A) light and (B) light.

3. The tracing must be in exact (A) with the paper during (B).

4. Blueprints could be washed in a basin of clean water as well as in a running water bath. (True or False)

5. What will happen if small particles of dirt remain on the glass during exposure? What will happen if you stand so that you cast a shadow on the glass during exposure?

6. What will happen if the contact between the tracing and blueprint paper is not perfect?

Fig. 252C. Continuous Printer
(Courtesy, Eugene Dietzgen Company)

Graphs and Charts

Graphs are useful to everyone. To be able to make them as well as understand them is doubly useful. There are so many kinds of reading matter that show graphs, charts, and diagrams that it would seem desirable to learn a few things about them.

Columns of figures are not easy to follow without close study, but if relative values of figures can be placed in the form of a graph, they can be understood at a glance. No matter how accurately a column of figures may represent the facts, the figures seem to be lacking in the power to convey meaning in the way that can be done by a graph.

Everyone is busy at his own occupation and the concentration required to read a column of figures will cause much good information to be passed unread. But make a graph of these figures, so they can be read easily, quickly, and clearly and people will get a picture of the facts with little effort. Of course the graphs must be the correct ones for the facts at hand; and the graphs must be made properly.

Graphs have been in use for centuries as a means of conveying facts quickly. In 1637 Descartes used the graph in representing the values of numbers. In 1783, a German named Chrome produced a book in which graphs were used to compare sizes of European states. William Playfair, a statistician in England, in 1786 gave to the public the first book using graphs to interpret meanings in business and banking. About this time, a statistician named Beaufort, in France, used graphs in describing certain statistical data.

The importance of graphs has grown to such an extent that today a number of books on the subject are available, and courses in making graphs, charts, and diagrams, are offered in nearly all colleges and universities. Engineers use graphs in solving mathematical problems. All professional groups use graphs in one way or another.

There are so many kinds of graphs that it seems best to attempt to show how to make only the most common ones. They are the line graph, bar graph, and area graph. Most other graphs are variations of these.

Questions

1. Why are graphs often used instead of large columns of figures?
2. Graphs are quite new and therefore they are not used a great deal in modern business. (True or False)
3. It is possible to use a type of graph that does not show the facts as well as another. (True or False)

Drawing a Line Graph

In Fig. 253 is shown a line graph, the principle upon which nearly all graphs are based. In Table IV is shown the figures from which the graph was made. The table is not the original, but it is presented to show the relationship of the figures to the graph. Study the irregular line in Fig. 253 and note how much more clearly the story is told in the graph than in the table.

In Fig. 256 observe how, at a glance, a baseball manager could follow the batting of each member of a team. It reads: In the first game, two hits were obtained; in the second game, one hit; in the third game, three hits. From the fifth game on, the opposing batteries seem to have found him out and he made no more hits. Now, were not quite a number of words used to tell

Table IV
**INCREASE IN ATTENDANCE AT BOYS
CLUBS 1944-1960**

YEARS	1944	1946	1948	1950	1952	1954	1956	1958	1960
BOYS	91	136	143	117	104	106	154	157	161

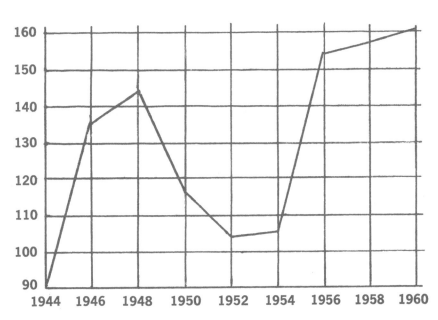

Fig 253. Increase in Attendance at Boys Clubs
1944-1960

the story? How much better and quicker it is told in a graph. The method of making a graph is as follows:

1. The graph is formed by plotting two figures in relation to each other on an axis. Two lines form this axis. They are at right angles to each other, Fig. 254. The horizontal line is called the *X* axis, or *abscissa,* and the vertical line is called the *Y* axis, or *ordinate.* The point of intersection of these lines is called the *origin.*

2. If two figures, or two sets of figures, are to be compared by means of a graph, they can be plotted from a form as shown in Fig. 254, by placing one set of figures on one axis and the other set on the other axis, at uniform distances. In order that the figures will be accurately placed, lines are first marked off on the paper. These lines are called the *grid,* Fig. 255.

3. Lay off the grid to represent uniform amounts in whatever set of figures is to be used on each axis. Even numbers serve best

as units, such at 2, 4, 10, 20, 30, 40, 50, and 100 and so on. Examine Fig. 253 and note how units of 10 and 2 are used.

4. Place numbers representing constant occurring things on the X axis. For example, in Fig. 256, the number of games played is the *constant.* Place numbers representing things that tend to change, *variables,* on the Y axis as, for example, the hits of the baseball rookie. In Fig. 258, time is the constant and years are the variables.

5. Let us plot, as in Fig. 255, the figures that are necessary to make the graph line in Fig. 256. The player made two hits during the first game, so 2 and 1 are plotted in relation to each other and a point located to represent them. Then plat each game and its number of hits until all figures are paired and plotted on the grid.

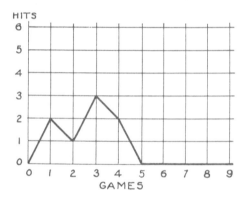

Fig. 256. Batting Record of a Rookie in the American Association

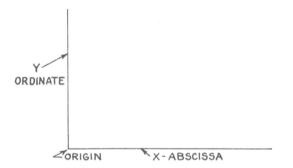

Fig. 254. Lines of a Graph

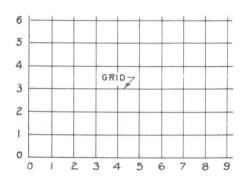

Fig. 255. Grid for a Line Graph

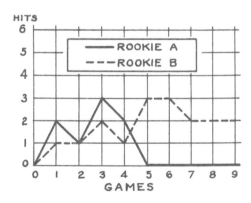

Fig. 257. Batting Record of Two Rookies in the American Association

6. Draw a line, equal in weight to an object outline, through each point. Draw the line straight from point to point.

7. Several sets of figures can be compared on one graph, but the graph lines representing each set must be made differently. In Fig. 257 two players are compared — one by a solid line and one by a dash line.

8. A key to the lines must be made so the reader can make the comparisons properly. The key may be arranged in a frame as in Fig. 257, or each line may be labeled with the proper name or letter. Sometimes the names or identifications are long so the frame generally serves best.

9. There must be a title. The title should be brief but clear. Unnecessary words should be avoided. For example, it is not necessary to say "Graph Showing Batting Record of a Rookie." It is understood that there is a graph. Only the words "Batting Record of a Rookie" are necessary.

10. If you secured the figures from which you made the graph from some other source than your own, place the source next to the horizontal row of figures, as in Fig. 253.

11. Graphs are referred to in books and magazines as Figures. (Fig.) See Figs. 253, 256, 257, and 258.

Questions

1. Why should the grid lines be placed evenly?

2. The point of intersection of the two lines (A) and (B) is called the (C).

3. Why would even numbers on the axis serve best in plotting?

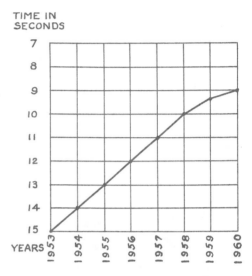

Fig. 258. My Swimming Record

65

Drawing a Bar Graph

Bar graphs, Figs. 259 and 260, are used to compare quantities or percentages, one with another. Each bar represents a quantity or percentage. Its length represents the amount of the quantity or percentage. Thus, in Fig. 259, a somewhat greater percentage of machines were installed in the Twin Cities than in the United States as a whole during a ten year period. In Fig. 260, one sees at a glance that R. Y. has not played as many games of baseball as have the other players. Fig. 259 shows percentages and Fig. 260 shows numbers or quantities.

Bar graphs are easy and interesting to draw if you have learned to draw the line graph. The bar graph can be drawn in various ways. In Figs. 262A and 262B, this graph is shown in a vertical position.

1. Draw a grid, or the background lines.
2. Select and draw the units that you propose to use in comparing the quantities or percentages. Use even amounts as in making the line graph. See Fig. 261.
3. Make the grid so there will be one line beyond the largest bar. For example, in Fig. 260, the 500 line goes beyond the bar that represents G.W. That is, the grid covers a range from a fixed point (zero in Fig. 260) to a point beyond the highest quantity or percentage.
4. Place the scale of values at the left of the vertical bar graph, Fig. 260, and at the top of horizontal bars, Fig. 259.

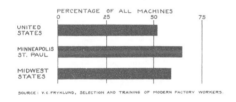

SOURCE: V.C FRYKLUND, SELECTION AND TRAINING OF MODERN FACTORY WORKERS.

Fig. 259. New Machines Appearing During a
Ten-Year Period

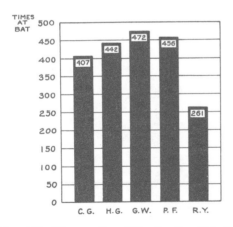

Fig. 260. Times at Bat of Five Leading Detroit
Batters as of August 27

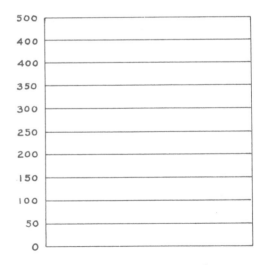

Fig. 261. Grid for a Bar Graph

5. Draw the bars on the grid by laying them off in relation to the scale of values. Examine Fig. 260 and observe the lengths of the bars in relation to the units to the left.

6. Space the bars so they will be separated a distance equal to half the full width of a bar. The bars in Fig. 259 are not well spaced. Start the first bar from the first grid line a distance equal to half a bar. **Space all the** bars evenly.

7. Place the labels or identifying marks under the vertical bars, Fig. 260, and at the left of horizontal bars, Fig. 259.

8. Fill in each bar solidly with black ink, or cross-hatch it.

9. Letter in the source as in drawing a line graph.

10. Place the title as in making a line graph.

Questions

1. Why is the grid necessary in laying out a bar graph?

2. Why would this type of graph, rather than a line graph, be most suitable for comparing percentages or quantities?

3. Why should the scale at the left of the graph in Fig. 260 be laid out uniformly?

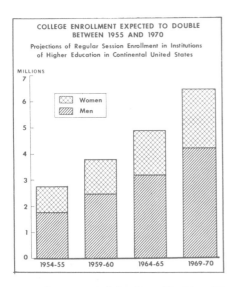

Fig. 262A. Showing Totals by Cross-Hatching (Courtesy, U.S. Department of Labor)

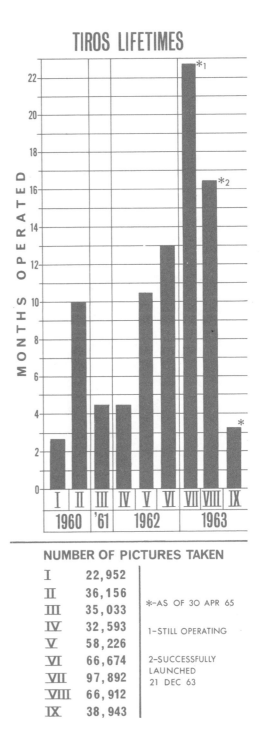

NUMBER OF PICTURES TAKEN		
I	22,952	
II	36,156	
III	35,033	*-AS OF 30 APR 65
IV	32,593	
V	58,226	1-STILL OPERATING
VI	66,674	
VII	97,892	2-SUCCESSFULLY
VIII	66,912	LAUNCHED
IX	38,943	21 DEC 63

Fig. 262B. Increase in Durability of TIROS Weather Satellites Numbers I through IX (Courtesy, NASA)

Drawing an Area Graph

The most common of the area graphs is the pie diagram. It takes its name from its shape, Fig. 263. There are many other types of area diagrams. In fact, the opportunities for originality are endless. It is important, however, in drawing an area diagram that the area drawn to represent one group shall be in proportion to the area drawn to represent the other group as is shown in Figs. 263, 264, and 265A.

The pie diagram is divided on the percentage basis. It does not readily divide into numbers.

To make a pie diagram:

1. Draw a circle of desired size.

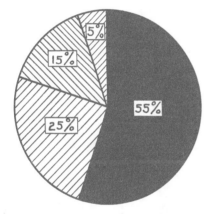

Fig. 263. Area Graph, Pie Diagram

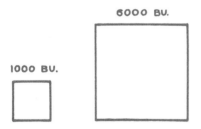

Fig. 264. Area Graph

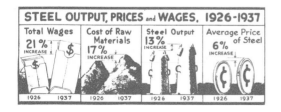

Fig. 265A. Picture Graphs Suitable for General Reports

EMPLOYMENT IN SELECTED MAINTENANCE AND REPAIR OCCUPATIONS . . . .

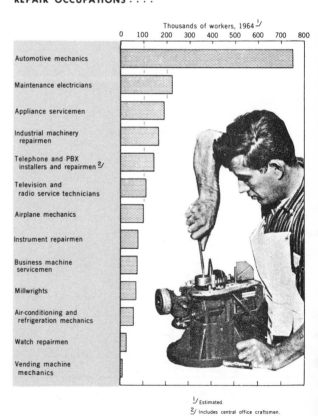

Fig. 265B. Graphs in Picture Form are not Suitable for Scientific Data (Courtesy, U.S. Department of Labor)

2. Let the circle represent 100%: that is, 360 degrees would equal 100%.

3. One per cent equals 360 degrees divided by 100. Therefore, allow 3.6 degrees for every single percentage unit marked on the circumference.

4. Suppose you wish to lay off a 55% slice on the pie. See Fig. 263. In degrees, this is 55 x 3.6, or 195 degrees. Lay off 195 degrees on the circle. Start at a point directly above the center and work to the right. If there are several percentages, use the largest one first and continue to the smallest.

5. Fill each segment with alternate cross-hatching and in solid black.

6. Leave a white space in a frame (a window) in which to label each slice.

7. The title will be the same as in making a line graph.

PROBLEMS

Problems — Line Graph

1. Plot your own batting according to hits, strikeouts, and walks. Make one graph showing all three.

2. Plot your golf game, or your tennis game.

3. Plan a line graph showing the sales, day by day, of your school in the Christmas seal campaign.

4. Plot all your grades for all courses by months (or terms) for last year.

Problems — Bar Graphs

1. Draw a bar graph showing the grades in drawing, by letters, given to your class on the last report cards. Ask your instructor for the total number of each letter grade given to the class.

2. Keep your favorite team record and work out bar graphs to show certain interesting comparisons.

3. Make a bar graph for the following table from the Smith Company showing a comparison of earning by 10 year periods.

Year	Thousand Dollars
1930	80
1940	150
1950	190
1960	85

Problems — Area Graphs

1. Make a pie chart that shows the percentages of supplies left in the scout commissary after one week of camp. There are 100 bushels of vegetables of which 42 are potatoes, 25 are carrots, 20 are beans, 10 are beets, and 3 are onions.

2. Make a pie chart covering any problem of your own.

The Civil Engineer and the Map Draftsman

Map making, surveying highways and railroads, planning and building bridges and dams are among the many duties that belong to the work of the civil engineer. There are many more things that he does, however. The civil engineer employed by a city also has to plan for sewer and water mains and paving. Any one of these requires ability to operate certain instruments of which the *transit* is the most difficult. With surveying instruments and a notebook, the engineers gather data from which plans are made. Most of the plans are maps of some kind.

For several years, the work of the civil engineer was limited. However at present, the outlook

Golden Gate Bridge (Courtesy, San Francisco Chamber of Commerce)

215

for employment in civil engineering is considered good with the increase of urban development which includes detailed surveys for water and sewer layout, water conservation and flood control projects, and highways. Civil engineering is one of the oldest of engineering careers and holds fascination for young men who like creative assignments outdoors and in new areas.[1] One must be an outstanding student with high ability

in mathematics and drawing to qualify for a position. Many civil engineers become very successful at map making and specialize in that work.

The civil engineer must have college training which usually covers a four-year period. Much of his work is outside, and while the duties are strenuous, they are healthful. The time devoted to work indoors generally involves the making of maps and drawings from field notes.

Computers are also used in civil engineering especially in design work, field data studies and in preparation of specifications.

[1]Bureau of Labor Statistics, U.S. Department of Labor: Washington, D.C., 1968-69. Bulletin No. 1550.

Drawing a Map

68

The branch of civil engineering that has to do with gathering field data for various kinds of maps is known as surveying. One type of map is shown in Fig. 266. Here a few of the various symbols shown in Fig. 267 are used because the scale of the drawing makes necessary the standard symbols to represent various things that cannot be shown in full size.

The map draftsman works from the field notes of the surveyor. The surveyor gathers field data with the aid of the *transit*. It is similar in appearance to a telescope, and it is mounted on a tripod. With the transit, vertical and horizontal measurements of angles can be made. A compass is part of the equipment of a transit so that measurements may be in relation to north and south.

When gathering data for a topographical map — making a survey — the surveyor makes a circuit of straight lines called a *traverse*, through the area to be mapped. This circuit is made with a transit and a tape called a *chain*. The angles and distances are recorded in the field notes, and a sketch is made. The traverse circuit ends at the starting point when an area is to be mapped. This makes possible a checking for accuracy.

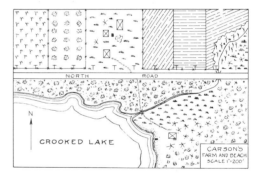

Fig. 266. Map

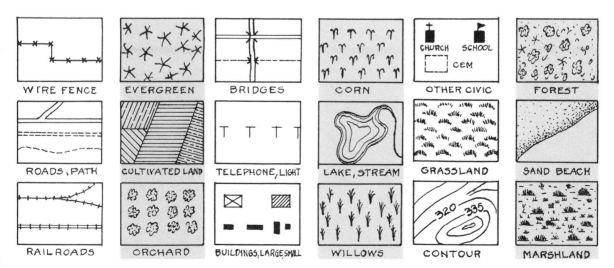

Fig. 267. Map Symbols

217

Traverses are also used in plotting rivers, lakes, and roads.

In Fig. 268 is shown a traverse circuit. After the traverse has been recorded, the surveyor goes over it again and makes observation and takes further notes. (See the field notes for Cullen's Landing.) The distance from station to station in a traverse is called a *course*. The important points on each side of course are recorded by means of *side shots* with the transit. These side shots are taken according to *angle* and *direction* in relation to north and south. When you examine a map, note that *North* is at the top.

Field Notes for Cullen's Landing

Course	Distance	Bearing	From
1-2	424 ft.	N 64° E	Monument
2-3	320 ft.	S 30° E	Iron stake
3-4	301 ft.	N-89°-30′ E	Intersection of Road and R.R.
4-5	490 ft.	S 70° W	Center of R.R.
5-1	459.5 ft.	N 56°-7′ W	Monument

Laying Out a Traverse

The compass on the transit, as all compasses, is graduated in degrees. It is divided into four equal parts called *quadrants*, Fig. 269, each of which is graduated from 0° to 90°. North and South are zero points. East and west are 90°

points. A bearing N. 64° E. is taken by sighting north and then east at an angle of 64°. A bearing S. 70° W. is taken by sighting south and then west at an angle of 70°.

Plotting a Bearing

1. To plot a bearing, such as N. 64° E. shown in the field notes for Cullen's Landing, draw a N. and S. line through the station point. Place a six-inch protractor, or a larger one, with its center on the station point as in Fig. 270. Let the straight side of the protractor fall on the N. and S. line. The straight side of the protractor must always be north and south when plotting. With a sharp pencil lay off 64° to the east.

2. Draw a straight line of indefinite length from station *1* through the 64° point. Lay off 224 feet on this line locating station *2*.

3. To lay off S. 30° E. draw a N-S line through station *2*. Place the center of the protractor

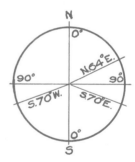

Fig. 269.   Compass Quadrants

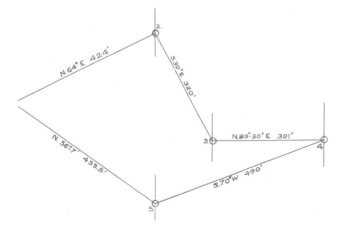

Fig. 268.   Traverse of Cullens Landing Scale ¼″ = 100′

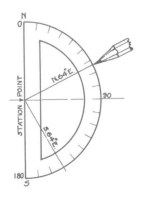

Fig. 270.   Plotting a Bearing

on station *2* with the straight side on the south line. Lay off 30° to the east.

4. Draw a straight line indefinite in length from station *2* through the 30° point. Lay off 220 feet on this line locating station *3*.

5. Continue from point *3* to *4* and so on from station to station until station *1* is reached again. If no mistakes have been made, the line from station *5* to station *1* will touch the starting point exactly.

Plotting Details From Traverse Points

1. Refer to the field notes and sketch, Fig. 271, for the survey of Cullen's Landing. Start at station *1*. The barbed wire fence runs due north and due west. The railroad runs through a point 150 feet due south and 210 feet on the line of traverse from station *1* to *5*.

2. Side-shot from station *2*. The U. S. highway is on the course from stations *2* and *3*. Points on the lake are N. 60° E.-118 feet; N. 90° E.-100 feet; S. 60° E.-123 feet. Locate the north corner of the school house S. 51°-30′ W.-123 feet. The north corner of the highway storage house is due south 148 feet.

3. Move to station *3*. Locate lake points by measuring due N.-172 feet; N. 30° E.-116 feet; N. 60° E.-152 feet.

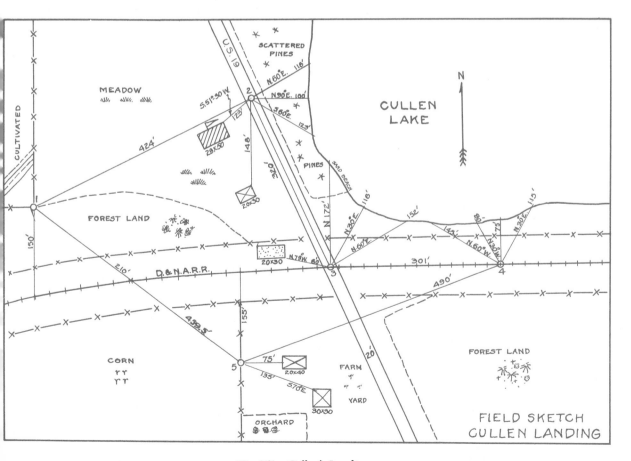

Fig. 271. Cullen's Landing

4. Move to station *4*. Locate lake points by measuring N. 60°-W. 145 feet, N. 30°-W. 80 feet, due N. 75 feet, N. 30°-E. 115 feet.

5. Go to station 5. The NW. corner of the house is S. 70° E.-135 feet. The west center of the barn is 75 feet due east. A barbed wire fence runs north and south through station 5. The R.R. is 155 feet north.

6. The R.R. right-of-way is 100 feet wide.

7. Draw in the lake, buildings, road, railroad, fences, trees, etc., as located, using all necessary symbols. It is not necessary to draw lines to show vegetation boundaries.

8. Letter the names of the lake, road, and railroad. Draw an arrow to show **direction** of north. Leave out all figures for bearings and distances. Letter the scale. Your drawing when complete should appear like the drawing in Fig. 266.

9. Check the drawing.

Questions

1. Why should a large protractor be used in plotting?

2. Why place an arrow for the north point when various north and south bearings are already given?

3. How would accuracy of the traverse be determined?

4. Why hold the protractor so that north and south lie along the straight edge?

Problems

1. With the directions given for drawing the traverse and details of an area, draw a map of Cullen's Siding, on 9″ x 12″ paper. Scale, 1″-100′.

2. Consult your Boy Scout Manual and learn to pace. Then select an area for mapping. From the data you obtain, draw a map.

The Architect

69

The architect is a professional man whose services can be compared with those of the doctor, lawyer, engineer, and scientist. He is a person whose services consist of designing, estimating costs, making drawings and specifications, preparing contracts between the builder and owner, and supervising construction of building. These duties all require special abilities and training that the owner seldom possesses and, therefore, the services of an architect are necessary.

To design a building with pleasing lines and proportions and of practical utility, the architect must have a feeling for the beautiful and the useful. He should be able to originate designs of buildings. He should know the work of the various craftsmen, such as carpenters, masons, plumbers, and electricians and be able to recognize when their work is carried on properly. He should understand structural design, which includes an understanding of stresses and strains.

High School Building — General Drawings Covered Sixty-Nine 36″ x 54″ Drawing Sheets (Courtesy, Bloomington Public Schools)

He should be able to estimate and do cost accounting. Then, there is the work that all of us think about when the word *architect* comes to mind; and that is, the making of blueprints, the drawing, tracings, and lettering that precedes the blueprint.

The architect is not called upon frequently for planning small homes costing near $15,000, although his services are as helpful in such building as in higher cost construction. So many houses of small cost are lacking in design. A house of low cost can be designed more readily than can one of high cost. There is less structure to take into account.

Most architectural work involves large buildings. When architects prepare plans and specifications but do not supervise construction, they receive from two to five per cent of the cost of

construction. When they supervise construction as well as prepare plans and specifications, they receive commissions ranging from six to ten per cent of the cost of construction. The 1964 yearly income for many architects throughout the country, and including various sizes of cities, was estimated at $25,000 or more.[1]

However, many architects receive much more than that amount. At 8% the architect's fees on a building costing $500,000 would be $40,000. From this amount he must pay his assistants, office rent, and other costs. Some architects specialize on large structures. The architect who works only on residences would require a rather busy year to keep his income above $20,000.

Young men find the fascination of the work, rather than the income, to be its chief attraction. The early years of service are quite certain to be as lean as are those of the doctor or lawyer. However, the creative nature of the work attracts persons with certain abilities and interests who

[1]U.S. Department of Labor, Washington, D.C.: 1966-67, Bulletin No. 1550, p. 203ff.

Industrial Building – A Prize-Winning Design (Courtesy, General Electric Company)

prefer to stay in it even though there are lean years. There is joy and satisfaction in designing and planning and supervising and seeing the creation of charm and utility that results from one's efforts. An architect is always creating and leaving, for generations that follow, evidence of his work.

Training to become an architect begins in high school and continues through college. Art and drafting courses and all mathematics courses in high school mark the beginning of architectural training. It is in these courses that one learns whether he likes to do such work and whether he can succeed in it. Also, in high school, history, English, languages, and sciences and mathematics are necessary in preparing the way for college training. Free-hand drawing, mechanical drawing, and art also are necessary. In these courses, the student should learn to do very exact work in drawing and in lettering. This is more necessary in the beginning than is training in building design because it is essential that work in design courses, later in college, be perfectly executed.

In 1966, there were 78 colleges and universities that offered courses in architecture. All are accredited by The National Architectural Accrediting Board whose purpose it is to maintain and develop a high standard of training. The average course in architecture is four years beyond

high school, and some colleges now require five years. Post-graduate college courses are also offered in architecture. Some students, who can afford it, extend their training to include study in Europe in gaining first-hand knowledge of the great architectural achievements of the past.

Successful architects recommend that a young man in training should work during vacations in an architect's office and in building construction. The college courses would then have more meaning. When the college course has been completed, the practical phases of the work are learned by working in an architect's office for many months. This is considered part of the training. According to men who have been interviewed, the length of time in an architect's office, before one establishes his own business, varies from two to ten years. Of course, not all young men establish practices of their own. Some prefer to continue to work in an architect's office.

The pay for workers in architectural offices in 1966, according to the U. S. Bureau of Labor Statistics[2], was $100 to $150 per week for new graduates. Experienced men were paid $150 to $250 per week. Yearly bonuses are often given.

The professional organization of architects is the American Institute of Architects. This association, as other professional associations, strives to maintain professional ethics and high standards of work. Most successful architects are members and take pride in making known their A.I.A. membership.

[2]*Ibid.*

The architect assumes responsibility for representing the owner in all activities that have to do with designing and supervising construction of a building. The architect must know his client's building needs and his financial rating. During the first consultation, the client should give information regarding the amount of money available for building, the kind of building required, and the lot on which it is to be located. Work on preliminary sketches is agreed upon and the drawings are started. When the sketches have been approved by the client, a contract is signed with the architect for working drawings, specifications, and supervision of construction of the building. The architect sells his services rather than the plans and specifications. The latter remain the property of the architect.

The working drawings and the specifications serve as the contract documents. When they have been approved, contractors are asked to examine them. Estimates of the costs are made and submitted as bids. After all the bids are received, the client and architect select the contractor, usually the one whose bid is lowest. The builder and owner then sign a contract to construct the house at the bid certain price.

As construction starts, there begins an important part of the architect's services. The architect inspects the construction and as the owner's agent, he sees that the plans and specifications are followed. Changes that become necessary must be approved by the architect and the owner. As the work progresses, the architect authorizes payment, by the owner to the builder, of part of the contract price. When the work is completed and approved, the final payment is made by the client.

The work of designing, making drawings, writing the specifications, and supervising the construction is very technical in nature — as might be supposed when the extensive training required of the architect is considered. The prospective owner needs these services. In many cases the charges for such services are offset by the savings and satisfaction of work well done.

Questions

1. Why is it necessary to have an architect as an agent in building a home in the same way as to have a doctor or lawyer for other purposes?
2. Why should changes that seem necessary during the construction of a building be approved by the architect and the owner before such changes can be made?
3. What are some of the difficulties that might arise if the owner attempted to be without the services of an architect?

Homes of Good Design

Understanding of good design comes with study and from observing good design. Development in knowing homes of good design is possible by comparing such homes. One must be exposed to the best in order to gain appreciation of it. It is a matter of growth. A well designed home has good exterior appearance, a good interior arrangement, and good construction. The exterior is viewed constantly by the neighbors and those who pass by, and therefore, it must be pleasing. The interior is seen and used by the family, so the arrangement of the rooms should meet the needs and comforts of those who live in it. Good construction adds to the lasting appearance of the home.

A well designed home has good balance and proportion. Compare Figs. 272 and 273. A well designed home has character. The details should be in proper relation to the whole structure and should be in harmony with the design of the home. They should belong, and not appear to be extras. Materials used in construction must be carefully selected and properly used. Simplicity in design is more desirable than is extensive decoration.

The interior of the home should be arranged to suit the activities that take place within and should be decorated in good taste. For example, the kitchen should be arranged so all necessary equipment is placed for most convenient service. There should be good light and good ventilation. The floor covering will receive constant wear and, therefore, it must be durable. With all mechanical arrangements properly made for convenience, there also must be pleasing decoration. The kitchen is the most used room in the home and, therefore, should be carefully planned.

The arrangement of the rooms is important in good design, and their purposes and uses should determine their location. The sizes of rooms are determined by the furniture and the amount of floor space desired. Rooms that are used together should be placed together, as for example, the kitchen and dining room.

Good construction is important in the execution of good design because the exterior and interior wall surfaces require a permanent base, and the design expected from the plans can only be obtained through good workmanship.

Many people do not know the principles of design and construction; therefore, as in employ-

Fig. 272. Good Design   Fig. 273. Poor Design

ing a lawyer or doctor, they employ an architect to advise them, prepare plans, and supervise construction.

In designing a home, the interior generally is given first consideration. Perhaps this happens because people think of immediate needs first. However, it would be well to think of the type of architecture desired on the outside at the same time that one plans the inside. Room arrangements for a *Colonial* house go best with a Colonial exterior. The Colonial house is formal both inside and outside. The stairway is placed in the center of a large hall leading to it. The dining room is located on one side of the central hall and the living room on the other. There is balance both inside and outside. It has a gable roof, narrow box cornice, green shutters on the windows that help to make more attractive the white paint of the wide siding. In Fig. 272 is shown a New England Colonial.

The *English* type of architecture holds a place with the Colonial in popularity. It is unlike the colonial in that both the interior and exterior design can be free from formality. Materials used in the English house are of brick and stucco and timber. In the early homes the timber was real, but today the timbered effect is carried out with boards. Casement windows are used almost entirely. In Fig. 274 is shown a house of English design. Many variations are to be seen and many of these do not do justice to the charm of the original. Perhaps it is because architects have not been called upon for help in designing.

The *Mission* design appears in the typical Southwestern home, Fig. 275. Some call it Spanish and others like to call it the Pueblo because the Indians of the Southwest built houses of adobe that had plastered walls with flat roofs. The walls necessarily were thick because of the added strength required in mud construction. There were few doors, but there were arched openings between rooms. The smooth plaster outside covering was given colors of blue, yellow, and red in their lighter shades. These are now represented in the colors given the stucco in the modern mission home. Tile, generally red, is used as a roof covering. Arched entrance ways and casement windows are retained from the older mission patterns. This design is in little favor in other sections of the country.

The *Italian* house is of smooth stucco exterior with tile covered gable and hip roofs, Fig. 276. There generally is formal balance although the design lends itself to modifications. One is reminded of the colonial with stucco outside instead of siding. There are columns, shutters, and casement windows. It is not a common American home.

Fig. 274. English

Fig. 275. Spanish

A new type of house seems to be gaining in popularity. It is the *Modern* or Contemporary house. It is box-like with rectangular and, in some cases, semi-circular parts and with considerable space given to large casement windows. The materials generally are of brick, stucco, and glass. There is little attempt to gain formality in balance. Glass is prominent in partitions and outside wall construction as well as in the windows. The contemporary or present-day house is the result of an effort to bring about innovations in house design and construction that is assumed to make living healthier and happier. The idea of openness is encouraged, at the same time keeping in mind that there are conventions to be observed, clothes to be cared for, cooking and eating, all of which cannot be ignored when one thinks of the winds and rains. In Fig. 277 is shown a house of modern design.

These are only a few of the many types of American homes. As time passes, there is more and more tendency to modify the traditional designs, and here and there are found splendid combinations of the older ones carried out in good taste. Of course, there are many that have just been built without effort to plan carefully. These are usually lacking in charm. Perhaps, some day, there may be a typical American home. But as communications and travel become easier from one continent to another, there may never be a home that is typical of only one country.

Fig. 276. Italian

Fig. 277. Modern

Building Plans

There comes a time in everyone's life when there is strong interest in a home. The desire to own a home seems to be natural to most people, and even though many choose not to own, they take satisfaction in studying pictures and plans of homes in magazines and plan books. To be able to sketch and plan the home of one's dreams is an ability desired by most persons. To be able to plan the summer cabin as well as the permanent home offers opportunity for many happy moments. Not only is there pleasure in planning, but time spent in sketching and planning will prevent mistakes and save money in actual building.

Then, too, to be able to understand plans and to be able to read them is necessary in business as well as in home activity.

Examine the floor plans and elevations in Figs. 278, 279, 280, and 281, and locate the walls, doors, and windows. Observe how the various rooms are lettered so there will be no difficulty in locating the rooms when reading the plans. Plans are required for the basement and each floor. Elevations are required for each side of the house. Special drawings to large scale are required for built-in features, fireplace, and parts of special design. Note that dimensions are provided. You will recognize that the things you learned in sketching and mechanical drawing will be useful in making drawings for houses.

1. Plans and elevations are drawn to a scale of ¼″ or ⅛″ to the foot. The scale is shown on each drawing and is represented as follows: Scale—¼″=1′-0″ or Scale—⅛″=1′-0″.
2. A floor plan really is a sectional view of the building taken at the level of the windows.
3. A floor plan shows the general shape of the building as it would be seen from above at the window levels. There is shown the shape of the building, length, width, location of walls, windows, doors, location of special connections and equipment, and kinds of materials.
4. The thickness of the walls in wood construction is shown as 6″ on plans, although the sizes of material in the completed building are such as to make the actual thickness 5⅝″ on the outside walls and 5¼″ on the inside walls.
5. Dimensions of outer rooms on floor plans are given from the outside of the outer wall to the center of the partition. Inner rooms are dimensioned from center to center of partitions. The dimensions are lined up and grouped whenever possible as is done in mechanical drawing.
6. Sizes of doors and windows may be shown as in Figs. 278 and 280 or by a door and window schedule, as in Fig. 280A, instead of directly on the floor plan. When the schedule is used, the data required by the builder are assembled for convenient checking. Plans for larger homes usually include door and window schedules.

   Instead of giving dimension for doors and windows on the plans, a code letter or number is placed at the proper location on the plan and also is placed in the first column. The total number of the same size and description is then placed in the next column of the schedule. The last column, *Remarks*, may be used to identify the door or window by a current millwork catalogue number or by a detail drawing.

Questions

Study the plans in Fig. 278.
1. Name the rooms.
2. Locate the doors and tell the size of each. Are closet and room doors the same in size?

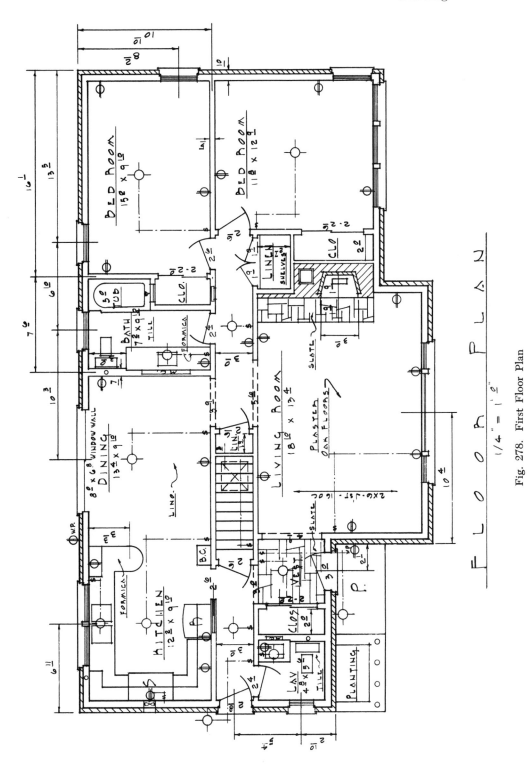

Fig. 278. First Floor Plan

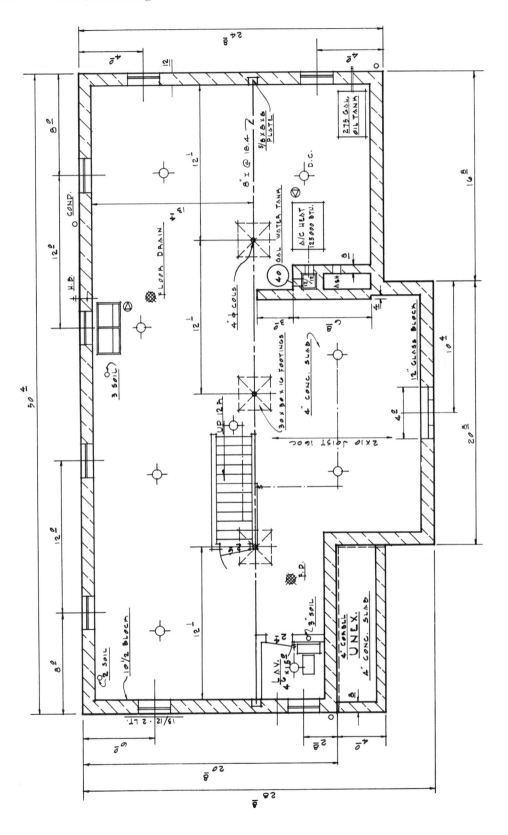

Fig. 279. Basement Plan

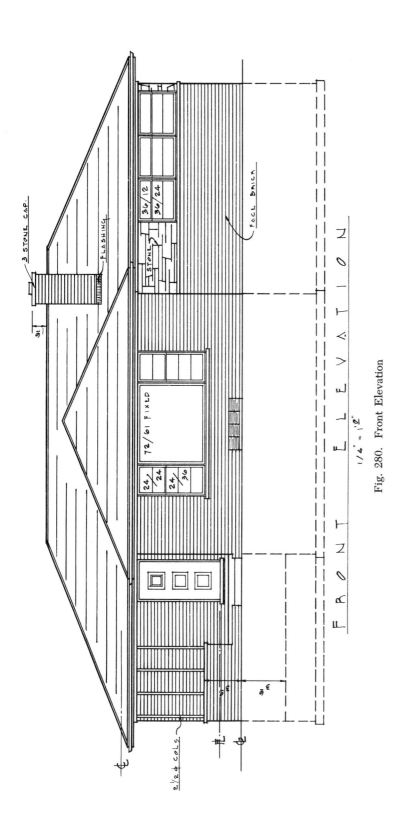

Fig. 280. Front Elevation

DOOR SCHEDULE

CODE	REQ.	SIZE	DESCRIPTION	REMARKS
A	1	3-0 x 7-0	Flush	M.W. Cat. #47
B	3	206 x 6-8	Panel	M.W. Cat. #49

WINDOW SCHEDULE

CODE	REQ.	SIZE	DESCRIPTION	REMARKS
E	2	24 x 24 / 24 x 36	D.H.	M.W. Cat. #83
F	5	36 x 12 / 36 x 24	D.H.	M.W. Cat. #84

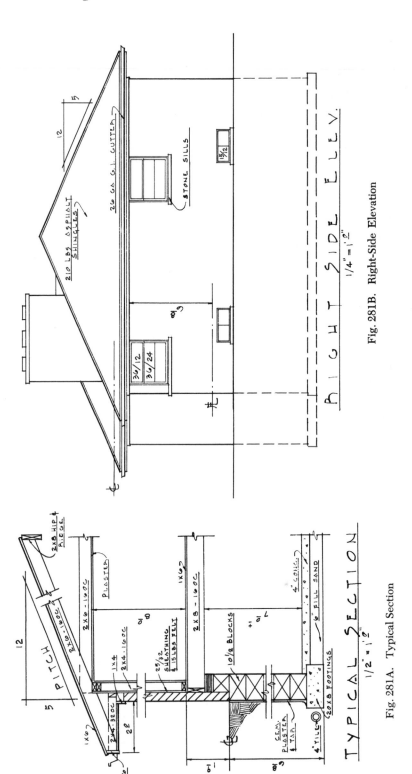

Fig. 281B. Right-Side Elevation

Fig. 281A. Typical Section

3. Locate the bath fixtures, kitchen cabinet, and sink.

4. How many electrical outlets are shown in the floor plan?

5. Locate the windows and give the sizes.

6. Examine Fig. 280 and determine which type of cornice is shown in the elevation.

7. Is there another location that could be used for the fireplace?

8. Measure pieces of furniture in your home and determine how it would be located in a house built from this plan.

9. Would it be a good idea to do this now so you could, if necessary, change locations of doors, windows, and fixtures on the plan?

Drawing a Floor Plan

1. Sketch the plan on cross-section paper, locating such features as doors, fixtures, cabinets, and the fireplace. Make changes that seem necessary as you study the room arrangements and details. See Fig. 282.

2. When you feel satisfied with the plan, determine the scale to which the plan must be drawn. If the structure to be drawn is small, or no larger than a house, use the quarter-inch scale.

3. Drawing paper 12″ x 18″ in size will be satisfactory for drawing a house plan, and paper 9″ x 12″ in size will be suitable for small structures such as garages, small cabins, play houses, or tourist cabins.

4. Examine the sketch in Fig. 282. Make such a sketch and add all horizontal dimensions, including thickness of walls and distances across rooms. Lay off the over-all dimensions and draw *lightly* line A in Fig. 283.

5. Add all vertical dimensions and lay off line B.

6. If the plan is to be square or rectangular and without projecting parts as in Fig. 284, continue to draw the outline as in drawing lines A and B.

7. If the plan is to be irregular in shape, with the same procedure as in steps 284, 285, and 286, lay off the various projecting parts.

8. Lay off the thickness of the outside walls and draw the necessary lines to indicate the outer wall, Fig. 285.

9. Locate the partitions with center lines by measuring the distances from the outside of outside walls to the center of partitions. Lay off the thickness of partitions by measuring half the thickness on each side of each center line, Fig. 286. Draw in the partitions.

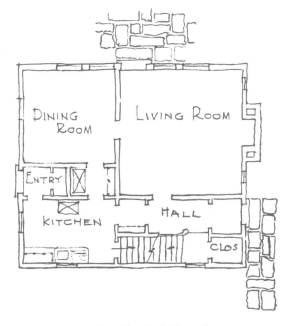

Fig. 282. Sketch of Floor Plan

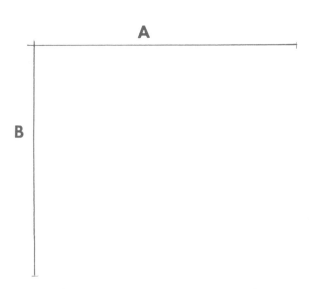

Fig. 283. First Step in Sketching Floor Plan

10. Locate the centers of doors and windows and draw a center line for each.

11. Lay off each door and window by measuring half its width on each side of its center line, Fig. 287. Windows are shown on plans four inches wider than the actual glass size. A window 20″ x 26″ is shown 24″ wide on the plan, Fig. 288. Doors are shown in actual width.

12. Examine Figs. 287, 288, and 289A, and observe how light connections and fixtures, bath fixtures, fireplace, and built-in cabinets are shown on the plans. The sizes for such features vary, and they are determined exactly from catalogues of special fixtures and millwork, and special drawings supplied by manufacturers. It is important that these details be placed and drawn to scale, but you need not dimension them. Such dimensions are given on special drawings, made to larger scale, or they are identified by catalogue numbers given in the specifications or on the drawings. The exact details of various features of a house cannot readily be drawn to

Fig. 284.   Second Step in Sketching Floor Plan

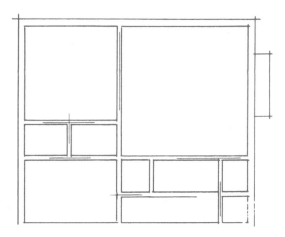

Fig. 286.   Fourth Step in Sketching Floor Plan

Fig. 285.   Third Step in Sketching Floor Plan

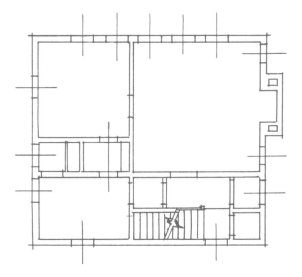

Fig. 287.   Fifth Step in Sketching Floor Plan

the small scale of a house plan, so symbols are used as shown in Fig. 289B.

13. Dimension all rooms as shown in Fig. 288. Draw light lines and neat arrowheads.

14. Add room and wall dimensions and see that they check with the over-all dimensions.

15. Go over all object lines with sharp black lines.

16. Letter the names of all rooms with capital letters $\frac{3}{16}''$ high. Letter all special notes and dimension figures in capital letters $\frac{1}{8}''$ high, Fig. 288.

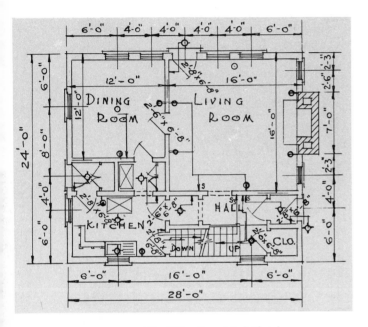

Fig. 288. Completed Sketch

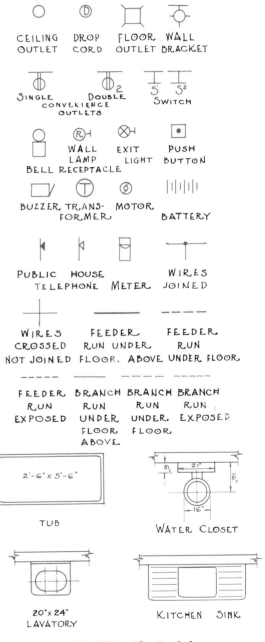

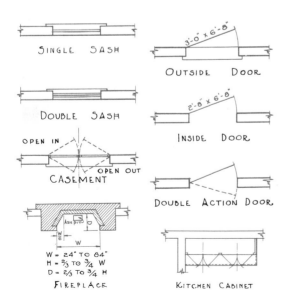

Fig. 289B. Plan Symbols

Fig. 289A. Plan Symbols

Fig. 289C. Playhouses (Courtesy, Los Angeles City Schools)

PROBLEMS

Arrange with your instructor for an assignment for drawing plans for a small structure. The following are suggestive:

1. Make sketches and draw a floor plan for a small structure. Suggestions are presented in Fig. 289C.

2. Make sketches and draw a floor plan for a tourist cabin 12′ x 16′ in size. Arrange for a door, three windows 20″ x 24″ double-hung, a clothes closet, a sink, and a kitchen cupboard.

3. Make sketches and plans for a summer cottage. There is to be a living room about 12′ x 18′ in size, a kitchen about 8′ x 10′ with a sink and kitchen cabinet, a bedroom 10′ x 10′ with a closet and a fireplace. Provide doors and windows as seem necessary.

4. Make sketches and plans for a small house with living room, dining room, kitchen, two bedrooms, and a bath. Study other plans, magazines, and books for ideas.

Drawing an Elevation

Examine the elevation in Fig. 292. An elevation is a view of a side of a building. It shows the shape of the walls and the roof. Windows, doors, eaves, gutters, downspouts, chimneys, fireplace, and kinds of materials are represented in their proper locations.

1. Sketch the elevation on cross-section paper locating openings, heights of floors and ceilings. Ceilings are usually 8'-6" to 9'-0" in height. Sketch lines representing the fireplace, porch, cornice, and roof. In making this sketch, take off the walls and openings from the sketch of the floor plan. When you have made sketches of all elevations and studied them carefully for locations of openings and so on, you should be ready to make the scaled drawing.

2. To draw an elevation, fasten the floor plan in position above the paper on which the elevation is to be drawn, Fig. 290. All center lines of openings and outside lines of walls are thus projected from the floor plan down to the elevation.

3. Draw a center line for the elevation and on it locate the heights of the ground, ceiling, and floor lines as determined in the sketch, Fig. 290.

4. From the floor plan project all center lines for all openings and all wall lines, Fig. 291.

5. Draw the cornice and the roof lines, Fig. 292.

6. Draw the windows, shutters, and doors.

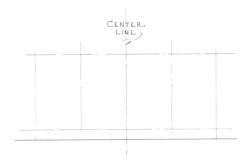

Fig. 291.   Second Step in Drawing an Elevation

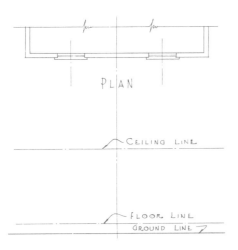

Fig. 290.   First Step in Drawing an Elevation

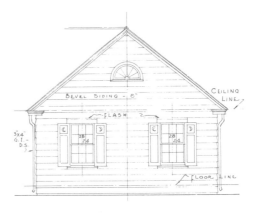

Fig. 292.   Completed Elevation

7. Draw the porch, steps, fireplace, and chimney as desired.

8. Draw representations of materials and give sizes of glass, siding, shingles, and special molding numbers.

9. Check the elevation to see that nothing is omitted.

10. Go over the outside lines and make them black.

11. Each elevation is made by following these directions.

Problems

Draw at least two elevations, front and side, for the floor plan you already have made.

Construction Details, Millwork, and Specifications

Construction details, and other details that appear in plans, books, and magazines, are drawn by the draftsman because the scale to which the floor plans and elevation are drawn is too small to permit accurate drawing of construction details. Therefore, larger scale details are drawn. It is intended here that the construction of the main parts of a house be studied, even though you may not draw them. Look at houses that are under construction and see if you can recognize the details drawn here. Remember that these details are only a few of the many that could be designed.

Foundations and Footings

Foundation walls are made of either concrete, brick, tile, or stone. Under the foundation wall are wider sections called footings that serve to better support the weight of the building. See Figs. 293A, 293B, 293C, 293D, and 293E. These footings vary in width according to the soil. A clay soil would not require footings as wide as

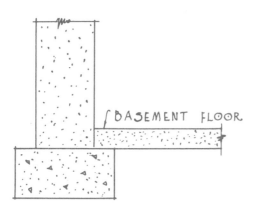

Fig. 293A. Concrete

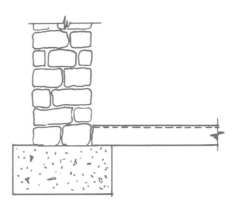

Fig. 293C. Stone

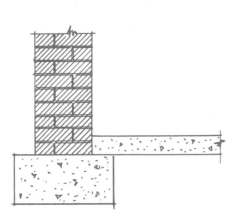

Fig. 293B. Brick

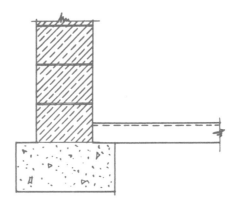

Fig. 293D. Concrete Block

would be required in loam. Footings almost always are made of concrete. For a house foundation they would be made twice as wide as the wall is thick, and as thick as the wall is thick. A

footing for an 8″ wall would be 16″ wide and 8″ thick. Footings are seldom used in house construction in a hard clay soil.

Sills

The sill is that part of a house that rests on the foundation and supports the walls and first floor. There are several ways of building a sill of which three common ones are shown in Figs. 294A, 294B, and 294C.

In Fig. 294B a sill detail is shown with a base and drip cap, or water table. In some sections of the country, this device is seldom used. The finish material, siding or stucco, is brought down to an inch below the top of the foundation to cover the joint, as in Fig. 294C. There are several methods of completing the sill, depending upon whether

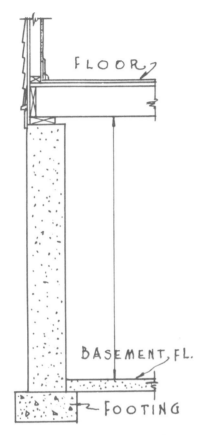

Fig. 293E. Basement Wall

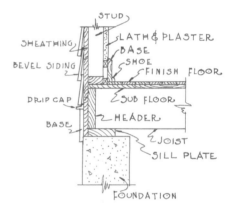

Fig. 294B. Sill

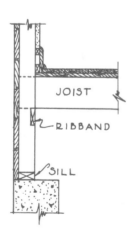

Fig. 294A. Sill

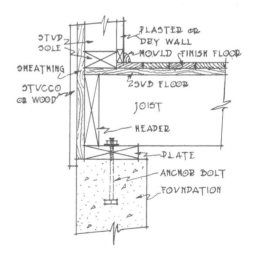

Fig. 294C. Sill

stucco, brick, or wood is used for finish material. You should determine what method is used in your area.

Cornices

The cornice is the upper part of the wall and the lower part of the roof framed together to seal the house from the weather and at the same time to add a finished appearance. There are two types of cornices, the open and the box, of which there are many variations. See Figs. 295A and 295B.

Roofs

There are several types of roofs as is shown in Fig. 296. The cornice is part of the roof. Roofs

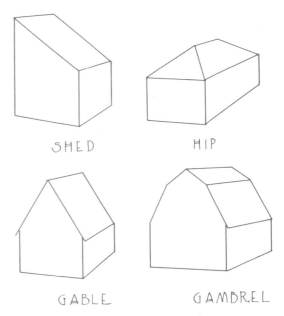

SHED   HIP

GABLE   GAMBREL

Fig. 296. Common Roofs

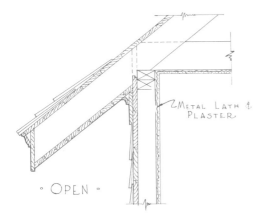

Fig. 295A. Open Cornice

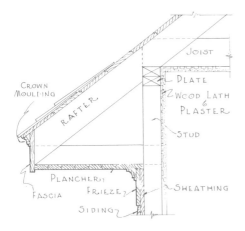

Fig. 295B. Box Cornice

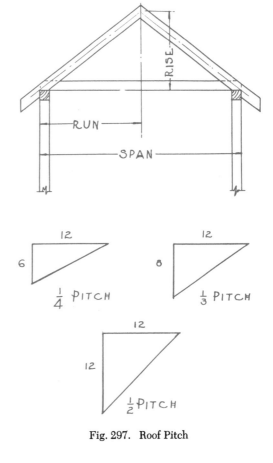

Fig. 297. Roof Pitch

may be constructed at various slopes in relation to the ceiling and wall. The slope of the roof is called the pitch. The pitch may be determined according to the design of the house. It is expressed as a fraction, and ⅓, ½, and ¼ pitch are common, although even steeper roofs are used in the newer homes. Pitch is obtained by finding the ratio of the rise of the roof to the span. See Fig. 297. In expressing pitch the span is always supposed to be 24'-0". The height or rise of a ½ pitch roof for a house 24'-0" wide would be 12'-0" at the ridge. The rise per foot of a ½ pitch roof, therefore, would be 0'-12"; and 12/24 is expressed as ½.

In laying out the slope of a roof, whatever the width of the building may be, you need only

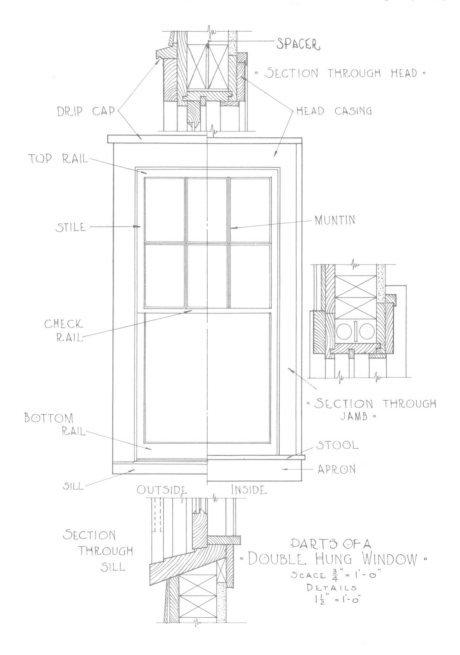

Fig. 298. Parts of a Double-Hung Window

measure 12 units in from the outer walls and then, from this location, measure vertically the number of units to give the pitch you desire. For example, by measuring 6 units vertically you would have ¼ pitch. Continue the roof line from the wall to the center line at the ridge, and the ridge will be the proper height for a building with a ¼ pitch roof and of whatever width.

Millwork

In every house there must be mouldings, windows, doors, window and door frames, window and door trim, and built-in cabinets. These are usually obtained in standard patterns and kept in stock by millwork and lumber companies. Ask your instructor to show you the Universal Millwork Design Book. It contains descriptions of standard millwork that may be purchased and identified by number in any part of the country. When standard trim is not used and special trim is made, the cost of a building increases. Cabinets are built in the house or they may be furnished by millwork companies.

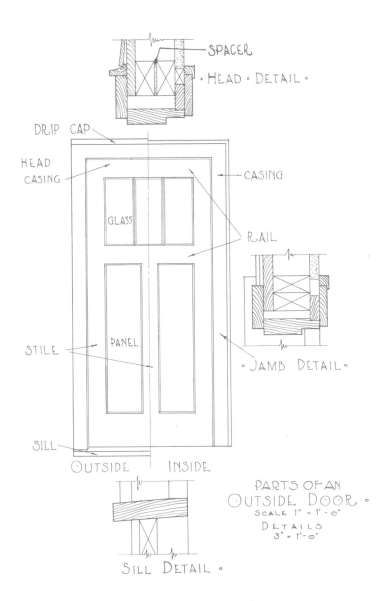

Fig. 299A. Parts of an Outside Door

Windows and Doors

There are two types of windows, the double-hung and the casement. A large scale drawing of a double-hung window is shown in Fig. 298. The glass in one sash may be in one piece or divided into several smaller panes. It would be well to know the names of the parts of a window so you can talk knowingly about it if it becomes necessary. Window sizes are indicated on plans by the glass size in one sash. Glass in windows may be had in certain sizes, and these sizes may be found in millwork catalogues.

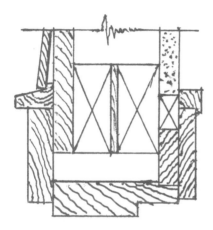

Fig. 299B. Cross Section Through Head
2 x 4s on edge have a furring strip between them.

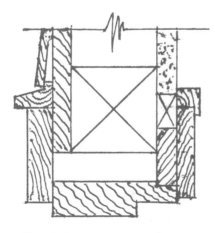

Fig. 299C. Cross Section Through Head
4 x 4s are used for single windows and doors, 4 x 6s for double, and 4 x 8s for wider openings, doors, or windows.

There are inside doors and outside doors, and they are available in various styles. The millwork book will show many beautiful doors in many sizes. Common sizes for inside doors are 2'-6" x 6'-8" and 2'-8" x 6'-8". Outside doors are usually 3'-0" wide and 6'-8" or 7'-0" in height. In Fig. 299A is shown details of construction for an outside door. See also Figs. 299B and 299C.

The section through the head of a window, Fig. 298, or the head of a door opening, Fig. 299A, may be encountered as shown in the details with the 2 x 4s laid flat, or the 2 x 4s may be placed on edge with a furring strip between them to match the width of the studding in the wall, Fig. 299B. In many sections of the country, the headings are 4 x 4s over single windows and doors; 4 x 6s over doubles, and 4 x 8s over wider openings, Fig. 299C. The latter is favored because it is strong and easily constructed. You will want to determine which method is used in your community.

Lumber

The lumber used in the framing of a house is of softwood. The interior millwork is usually of hardwood. Lumber is referred to as boards unless it is thicker than two inches, in which case it is called dimension lumber. Heavy timbers are excepted. Lumber is sold in standard sizes. The actual sizes delivered are less than the sizes given in the lumber order. For example 1" lumber is 13/16" thick; a 2 x 4 is 1¾" x 3¾". The widths are listed in units of two inches and the lengths in units of two feet. Common widths range from 2" to 14", and lengths range from 8' to 20'. Just as you list lumber in the school shops, so would you list it in ordering for building a house; that is, give the thickness, width, and length in order, 1" x 8" x 10'.

Specifications

There are many features of a house that cannot be drawn, but they can be described in writing so the builder will fully understand the requirements. Some materials and fixtures can be described fully in the specifications and need not be drawn. Most plans have little value in the courts of law without specifications to supplement them. Specifications are quite alike in form, but the content may vary because of differences in materials. For example, the differences in masonry and frame construction would change the content but not the form of specifications. Ask your instructor to show you a set of specifications. In addition to descriptions of materials, construction, and fixtures, specifications contain information that involves inspection, insurance, safety, payments, cleaning, occupancy, and many other details, all of which the builder agrees to follow when he signs the contract to build. You see, it is important to hire an architect who will attend to these matters. The home owner usually knows little about them. To accept plans and specifications made by the builder himself lessens the chances of the owner getting what he wants. There is no one to interpret the plans and to inspect the work in the owner's best interests.

Questions

1. Give as many reasons as you can why an architect should be employed to prepare plans and specifications for building a home.
2. Why is it necessary to have specifications as well as working drawings?
3. What does 2'-6" x 6'-8" mean when referring to a door?

PROBLEMS

1. Sketch the plan symbols for:

   1. switch   2. dropcord   3. wall bracket
   4. ceiling outlet.

2. Sketch the plan symbols for:

   1. Front door   2. Bathroom door
   3. Double-hung window   4. Bath tub
   5. Lavatory

3. In the following lumber descriptions there are several mistakes. Write them correctly.

   1. Pine, 12 pcs. 8″ x 1″ x 10′
   2. Pine, 8 pcs. 1″ x 6″ x 12′
   3. Pine, 16 pcs. 4″ x 12′ x 2″
   4. Pine, 14 pcs. 10′ x 4″ x 1″
   5. Pine, 6 pcs. 2″ x 16′ x 8″

4. In arithmetic, and in the shop, you may have learned to figure board measure. How many board feet are there in each of the above?

For Additional Study

Baer, Charles J., *Electrical and Electronics Drawing*. New York: McGraw-Hill Book Co., 1965.

Bellis, Hubert, and Walter Schmidt, *Blueprint Reading for the Construction Trades*. New York: McGraw-Hill Book Co., 1968.

Hepler, Donald E., and Paul I. Wallach, *Architecture: Drafting and Design*. New York: McGraw-Hill Book Co., 1965.

Lightle, R. Paul, *Blueprint Reading and Sketching*. Bloomington, Illinois: McKnight & McKnight Publishing Co., 1965.

Ray, J. Edgar, *Graphic Architectural Drafting*. Bloomington, Illinois: McKnight & McKnight Publishing Co., 1960.

Spence, William P., *Architecture: Design — Engineering — Drawing*. Bloomington, Illinois: McKnight & McKnight Publishing Co., 1967.

Steinike, Otto A., *Blueprint Reading, Checking, Testing*. Bloomington, Illinois: McKnight & McKnight Publishing Co., 1956.

Walraven, H. Dale, *Handbook of Engineering Graphics*. Bloomington, Illinois: McKnight & McKnight Publishing Co., 1965.

Wright, Lawrence S., *Drafting: Technical Communication*. Bloomington, Illinois: McKnight & McKnight Publishing Co., 1968.

Index